CW00663467

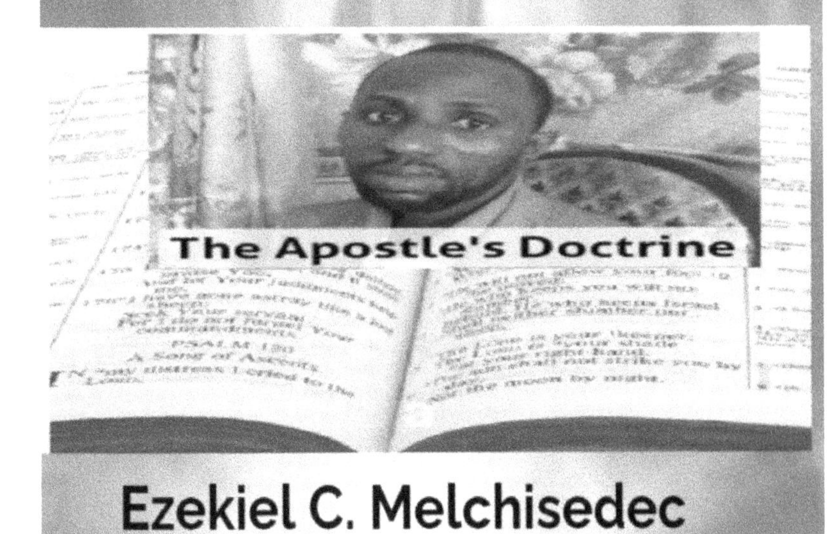
The Apostle's Doctrine
Ezekiel C. Melchisedec

The Apostle's Doctrine

Ezekiel C. Melchisedec

Published by Ezekiel Melchisedec publications, 2023.

THE APOSTLE'S DOCTRINE

First edition. September 5, 2023.

ISBN: 979-8223922605

Written by Ezekiel C. Melchisedec.

Also by Ezekiel C. Melchisedec

Season Two

Letters From God (Love of God)

Standalone

Discovering Godly Riches

Marriage According To God

The Prophetic Guide

Praying Against Demons

Marriage Pills

The Success Pro

Prophetic Prayer Companion

Prophetic Guide And Prayers

Understanding The Prophetic

New Testament Doctrine

Pastoral Etiquette

Letters From God Devotional

The Apostle's Doctrine

The Apostle's Doctrine ,
Ezekiel C. Melchisedec

Chapter 1 :
CONCEPT OF JUDGMENT

"For we must all appear before the judgment seat of Christ; that every one may receive the things done in his body, according to that he hath done, whether it be good or bad". 2 Corinthians 5:16.

Judgment basically is accountability to God on the final day. There is certainly going to be a day when we shall all appear before the judgment seat of God where we shall give account to God for all things we have ever done, good or evil. There and then God will hold us accountable for the good and or evil deeds that we ever did whilst we were on earth. It is accountability of whatever we did with our body or in our body or which we were alive in this body.

"For God shall bring every work into judgment with every recent secret thing, whether it be good or whether it be evil. Ecclesiastes 12:14. In judgment God is going to reward righteousness and punish sin as well. "and behold, I come quickly; and my reward is with me, to give every man according as his work shall be". Revelation 22:12

For everything that we have ever done God will bring it into account at the judgment because there are a hundred percent records of our deeds in God's book. *"and I saw the dead, small and great, stand before God, and the books were opened, which is the book of life: and the dead were judged out of those things which were written in the books, according to their works". Revelation 20:12*

Judgment therefore is the design of God to punish sinners and also to reward the righteous. *"And whosoever was not found written in the book of life was cast into the lake of fire. Revelation 20:15".* God's judgment for the unrepentant is to be condemned to eternal fire of destruction. In judgment we discover the terror of the Lord against the disobedient and the devil.

"Knowing therefore the terror of the Lord, we persuade men (people)". 2 Corinthians 5:11. This shows that God gives out judgment in fury, although he is a merciful God. However, at the judgment it is a terrifying scene, because then the time of mercy has exhausted. God's judgment without mercy will be at the end of the world and especially the judgment day.

CHAPTER 2: THE STIGMA OF SIN

" Some men's sins are open before hand, going before to judgment, and some men they follow after." 1 Timothy 5:24

Sin can be a stain that can be attached to you wherever you go and in whatever you do. This means the sin trails behind you and its gluing effect is always present whenever you find yourself . In fact it becomes a stigma and as such it is a spot and a blemish on your spiritual and physical personality. It is described as a filthy garment on you as in the case of Joshua the high priest.

" Now Joshua was clothed with filthy garments and stood before the angel... take away the filthy garments from him. And unto him he said, behold I have caused thine iniquity to pass from thee, and I will cloth thee with a change of garments ..." Zechariah 3-3-4 The evil that people do always follow them and as such it becomes part of their destiny, till they repent and receive Christ and have their sins forgiven. Then they are cleansed by the blood.

" And shall receive the reward of unrighteousness, as they that count it pleasure to riot in the day time. Spots they are and blemishes , sporting themselves with their own deceivings while they feast with you ." 2 Peter 2:13 When you take pleasure in sin ,it becomes a spot on your spiritual garment and that makes you unclean .It also brings disgraceful consequences at the end . Whenever you choose to disobey God's word , the act of sin committed is attached to you forever and that is the blemish on you.

On you Christ however used the word of God to take away the stigma from our lives. So we can be whole in order to receive salvation. *"That he might sanctify and cleanse it with the washing of water by the word. That he might, present it to himself a glorious church, not having spot or wrinkle, or any such thing; but it should be holy and without blemish".* Ephesians 5: 26 – 27. Speaking of the church as an entity is referring to the individual members (the Christians).

It is the blood of Jesus Christ and the word that actually can take the stigma of a lifetime that follows you because of your sins. *"But if we walk in the light, as he is in the light, we have fellowship one with another and the blood of Jesus Christ his son cleanseth us from all sin". 1 John 1: 7*

CHAPTER 3:
WHY WE SIN

"Now if I do that I would not, it is no more I that do it, but sin that dwelled in me." Romans 7: 20.

There are two basic reasons why we as human beings indulge in sin. The first and foremost reason is there is a law that brings restrictions and also forbids us to do so many things that we would like to do naturally.

For instance, the first time human beings sinned was when Adam and his wife disobeyed God's law, by eating the forbidden fruits (Genesis 3: 1 – 13). The law brings a temptation of disobedience and of course God's test of loyalty for us is obedience.

"What shall we say then? Is the law sin? God forbid Now, I had not known sin, but by the law, for I had not known lust, except the law had said, thou shalt not covet". Romans 7: 7. In other words, the law introduced sin. "For when no law is, there is no transgression". Romans 4: 15.

The second reason we sin is because there is a sinful nature in every human being and for that matter we are bound to commit sin. The tendency to do evil is present in the human heart and that is why God in his infinite wisdom gave us commandments. *"For the good that I, would I do not: but the evil which I would not, that I do"*

Romans 7: 19. The human nature has a flaw in itself, because it lacks the capacity to be good, rather it has the ability to do evil (i.e. bad things)

That is the reason we all need the savior, Our Lord Jesus Christ (Yeshua) to deliver us from the power of sin. *"For what the law could not do, in that it was weak through the flesh, God sending his own son in the likeness of sinful flesh and for sin, condemned sin in the flesh." Romans 8:2* This means the flesh is always weak, in the sense that it is always failing to abide by the rule of righteousness, which is the law.

Jesus therefore, having a strong flesh defeated the strength of the law by obedience, because he committed no sin in the days of his flesh.

"For he hath made him to be sin for us, who know no sin, that we might be made the righteousness of God in Him". (Christ) Romans 2: 5 – 21. You can actually overcome sin if you receive Christ into your heart. Those who have been saved have received grace to overcome the temptation of sin.

CHAPTER 4:
THE LAW AND SINNERS.

"Knowing this that the law is not made for a righteous man, but for the lawless and disobedient, for the ungodly and for sinners, for unholy and profane, for murderers of fathers and murderers of mothers. For man's layers". 1 Timothy 1: 9

The law certainly was introduced because of the sinfulness of the people. When there is no law people behave anyhow and they tend to whatever they deem fit for them to do. People usually misbehave whenever there is no law. Because, law brings restriction and prohibition, people cannot behave any how when there are laws.

As a result, there is always orderliness and harmony in the human society. God in his infinite wisdom gave us laws to keep us on the right track. The law has one sole purpose that is to establish love. Love for God and love your neighbor. *"For all the law is fulfilled in one word, even in this, thou shalt love thy neighbor as thyself". Galatians 5: 14.* The law therefore has to teach sinner how to love people.

"Wherefore the law was our school master to bring us into Christ, that we might be justified by faith". Galatians 3: 24. The law is meant to educate sinners, the way of righteousness revealed by love. This is true because if you love someone you will not steal from the person, you won't kill the person, you won't lie against the person, and you won't sleep with his wife or her husband. The law has a specific responsibility to instruct sinners on the way of righteousness.

The law gives sinners the knowledge of sin". *For by the law is the knowledge of sin". Romans 3: 20.* This means the law gives us information of what sin actually is, at least for a sinner to be able to distinguish between sin and righteousness. The unsaved person needs the law to clarify his or her state of affairs. To know whether you are righteous or sinner, it is the law that will bring you to that knowledge.

A person living in sin can be right in their own conscience, because every sinner has his or her own justifiable reasons for committing sins in their lives. Although the reason doesn't make a sinner right. It is therefore good for the sinner to identify with the law of God, so that he or she can discover the life of righteousness. *"For until the law sin was in the World: but sin is not inputted when there is no law". Romans 5: 13*

CHAPTER 5:
THE CONSEQUENCE OF SIN

"then I will walk contrary unto you also in fury; and I, even I, will chastise you seven times for your sins." Leviticus 26:28

Of course sin has a lot of consequences, in fact the gravity of sin and the aftermath effect of sin in the human life is enormous. Throughout the entire bible, especially the Old Testament we see how God punished the Israelites for their sins. In the opening scripture, God said he will chastise them seven times, seven symbolizes perfection, and this means God will give them the perfect punishment they deserve for their sins.

"Is not destruction to the wicked? And a strange punishment to the workers of iniquity?" Job 31:3 God really destroys the wicked at the end, yea that is their punishment.

The consequence of sin

People that refuse the word of God and continually disobey God's word by doing evil to their neighbor and said to be wicked people, and such people are usually destroyed at the end. The lord is a merciful God and wants people to be given a chance to repent, and this shows how merciful our God is.

However, when people refuse the way of righteousness and embrace sin, they are destroyed at the end. "*for the punishment of the iniquity of the daughter of my people is greater that the punishment of the sin of Sodom, that was overthrown as in a moment and no hands stayed on her*" Lamentation 4:6 God consumed the whole city of Sodom for their sin (Homosexuality and Lesbianism) with fire from heaven.

Sin makes God to turn against his people. In fact, God repented creating human beings because of sin. "*And God saw that the wickedness of man was great in the earth, and that every imagination of the thoughts of his heart was only evil continually. And it repented the Lord that he had made man on the earth, and it grieved him at his heart. And the Lord said, I will destroy man whom I have created from the face of the earth... for it repenteth me that I have made them." Gen. 6:5 – 7.*

That is the reason why we cannot endorse sin in our society, because it will incur the wrath of God upon human beings. In essence we ought to overcome the temptation of sin by using God's word. Whenever we tolerate sin in our lives, we should know that it brings destruction. In the days of Noah we see how God destroyed the whole world with flood, yet saved Noah and his family because of their righteousness.

CHAPTER 6:
CONCEPT OF RIGHTEOUSNESS

"And is shall be our righteousness if we observe to do all these commandments before the Lord our God, as he hath commanded us." Deuteronomy 6:25.

Righteousness is living right in the sight of God by doing what is right. This is a life without wrongdoing or evil behavior. Righteousness is the lifestyle of God for every human being to live up to. It is the standard of life God expects from the ordinary human being that was created by God. Among other things righteousness entails obeying the word of God and it is the exact opposite of sin (disobey God's word).

It is a pathway of God for us to follow as exemplified by Christ. *"For he hath made him to be sin for us, who I knew no sin; that we might be made the righteousness of God in him." (Christ) 2 Corinthians 5:21* Jesus is our perfect example of what righteousness is. This is the way of life that God wants all people to follow. *"He restoreth my soul; he leadeth me in the path of righteousness for his name's sake" Psalm 23:3*

Even faith in God is another form of righteousness, because we are commanded to have faith, so whenever you have faith you are obeying God's word and that is why it is a form of righteousness. *"But to him that worketh not, but believeth on him that justifieth the ungodly, his faith is courted for righteousness". Rom 4:5.* This is not saying righteous deeds are not necessary for salvation, but rather saying affirming faith in God is another form of righteousness.

In another scripture we are told to *"awake to righteousness, and sin not: for some have not the knowledge of God..."* so therefore when we live in righteousness we do not commit sin, because sin is unrighteousness. Righteousness is therefore a commitment to obeying God's word as much as possible. A person cannot be righteous if he or she is disobeying God's word.

The purpose of righteousness is to defeat sin in the human life so that God's kingdom will be established. *"And if Christ be in you, the body is dead because of sin; but the spirit if life because of righteousness". Romans 8:10.* God wants us to overcome sinful deeds by way of righteousness. To be a righteous person you must adhere to the commandments of God and obey them through faith in Christ Jesus our Lord and savior.

CHAPTER 7:
THE RIGHTEOUSNESS OF CHRIST

"For Christ is the end of the law for righteousness to everyone that believeth". Romans 10:4

The righteousness of Christ is the perfection of our Lord Jesus Christ (The Yahshua) that has been credited to the believer. This means that Christ Jesus lived a righteous life; a life without sin. Therefore, the righteousness of Christ is an account given to the believer once you give your life to Christ. We are made to receive Christ righteousness as a gift once we are born-again.

"for if by one man's offense death reigned by one; much more they which receive abundance of grace and of the gift of righteous shall reign in life by one, Jesus Christ" Romans 5:17. In this scripture it is clear that we use all affected by the sins of Adam that brought death to humanity. In order for God to counteract the sinful records of Adam against humanity, Christ came to credit us with righteousness. This means before Christ every human being on earth was seen as a sinner.

Therefore, Christ came to make as many as believe in him righteous by virtue of Christ righteousness. *"For the hath made him to be sin for us, who knew no sin; that we might be made the righteousness of God in him". 2 Corinthians 5:21.* This means there was an exchange, Christ took the place of our sin (including our sinful records), and he gave his righteousness as a gift. Therefore, the righteousness of Christ is credited to us not by our deeds but by faith in our Lord Jesus Christ.

"Therefore as by the offense of one judgment came upon all men to condemnation; even so by the righteousness of one the free gift came upon all men unto justification of life." Romans 5;18. The righteousness of Christ is what justifies the Christian regardless of their sinful past. Christ righteousness gave us the free gift (grace) and this gift gives us the sense of justification and assurance of salvation. Henceforth, we do not have our own righteousness but the righteousness *of ChrisT* .

"...not having mine own righteousness, which is of the law, but that which is through the faith of Christ, the righteousness which is of God by faith". Philippians 3:9. Now therefore we are entitled the righteousness of God by faith, which came through Christ Jesus.

CHAPTER 8:
THE RIGHTEOUS LIFE

"And it shall be our righteousness if we observe to do all these commandments before the Lord our God, as he hath commanded us in Deuteronomy 6:25.

The righteous life is certainly a requirement of God for the children of God. When you receive the righteousness of Christ, it will automatically yield the fruits of righteous life. *"That the righteousness of the law might be fulfilled in us, who walk not after the flesh, but after the spirit." Romans 8:4*

Righteousness is a strict requirement of God from every Christian. This means the righteous life ought to be a lifestyle.

"Bring forth therefore fruits meet for repentance." Mathew 3:8. The righteous life bears fruits of a good life, which is also formed as fruits

of the spirit in Galatians 5:22-23. *"But the fruit of the spirit is love, joy, peace, longsuffering, gentleness, goodness, faith, meekness, temperance against such there is no law".* The righteous life is a life that honors God's word. Living in obedience to the word of God.

In contrast is the ungodly life, also called wickedness. *"now the work of the flesh are these; Adultery, fornication, uncleanness, lasciviousness, idolatry, witchcraft, hatred, variance, emulations, wrath strife, seditions, heresies, envying, murders, drunkenness, reveling and such like; of the which I tell you before as I have also told you in time past that they which do such things shall not inherit the kingdom of God" Galatians 5:19-21.*

A righteous life does not do such things in the aforementioned scripture. The life of wickedness is all mentioned above anyone who indulges in right of God. The righteous life is possible when we receive grace from God to overcome the temptation of sin. *"For sin shall not have dominion over you for ye are not under the law but under grace". Romans 6:14.*

The righteous life, therefore, is a life of grace that enables us to overcome all the lures of sin and to be totally obedient to the word of righteousness.

CHAPTER 9 :
HARVEST OF RIGHTEOUSNESS

"Peacemakers who sow in peace reap a harvest of righteousness". James 3:18 NIV.

Righteousness is a seed of life, whenever you sow a life of righteousness, also known as fruits of righteousness. This is the kind of blessing you reap whenever you do the right thing by obeying the word of God. Righteousness is a life that brings rewards to the righteous at the right time.

"And let us not be weary in well doing for in due season we shall reap, if we faint not". Galatians 6:9. In this scripture the righteous is admonished to continue in their righteousness because there is a harvest to reap at the due time. This means there is a time to receive blessings from God because of our life of righteousness. In order to reap this harvest, we need to be persistent in the life of righteousness.

The good deeds we do in obedience to the word of God brings the reward called the harvest of righteousness, just as our sinful deed brings the punishment thereof. *"For he that soweth to his flesh shall of the flesh reap corruption; but he that soweth to the spirit shall of the spirit reap life everlasting". Galatians 6:8.* The harvest is more of eternal life but because that is the only thing that is incomparable to anything material.

These are people that do all kinds of sinful things in order to get material possessions such as wealth and properties. These people may cheat, kill, deceive, steal, lie, murder and commit all kinds of evil acts in order to acquire material things. But righteousness gives the righteous both material possession and eternal life which is more important for our soul.

"For bodily exercise profiteth little; but godliness is profitable unto all things, having promise of the life that now is, and of that which is to some" 1 timothy 4:8. The profit we set from the life of righteousness is the best because it caters for our material, spiritual and eternal needs. Jesus said *"seek ye first the kingdom of God and his righteousness; and all these things shall be added unto you". Mathew 6:3* Jesus was referring to food, drink and clothing when he said "all these things".

CHAPTER 10 :
CONCEPT OF JUDGMENT

"For we must all appear before the judgment seat of Christ; that every one may receive the things done in his body, according to that he hath done, whether it be good or bad". 2 Corinthians 5:16.

Judgment basically is accountability to God on the final day. There is certainly going to be a day when we shall all appear before the judgment seat of God where we shall give account to God for all things we have ever done, good or evil. There and then God will hold us accountable for the good and or evil deeds that we ever did whilst we were on earth. It is accountability of whatever we did with our body or in our body or which we were alive in this body.

"For God shall bring every work into judgment with every recent secret thing, whether it be good or whether it be evil. Ecclesiastes 12:14. In judgment God is going to reward righteousness and punish sin as well. *"and behold, I come quickly; and my reward is with me, to give every man according as his work shall be". Revelation 22:12*

For everything that we have ever done God will bring it into account at the judgment because there are a hundred percent records of our deeds in God's book. *"and I saw the dead, small and great, stand before God, and the books were opened, which is the book of life: and the dead were judged out of those things which were written in the books, according to their works". Revelation 20:12*

Judgment therefore is the design of God to punish sinners and also to reward the righteous. "And whosoever was not found written in the book of life was cast into the lake of fire. Revelation 20:15". God's judgment for the unrepentant is to be condemned to eternal fire of destruction. In judgment we discover the terror of the Lord against the disobedient and the devil.

"Knowing therefore the terror of the Lord, we persuade men (people)". 2 Corinthians 5:11. This shows that God gives out judgment in fury, although he is a merciful God. However, at the

judgment it is a terrifying scene, because then the time of mercy has exhausted. God's judgment without mercy will be at the end of the world and especially the judgment day.

CHAPTER 11
WHO FACES JUDGMENT?

"Because he hath appointed a day in which he will judge the world in righteousness..." Acts 17:31

The whole world will face the judgment of God on the last day. God has said in his word that we all shall appear before the judgment seat of Christ. There and then we shall give account to God for whatever life we chose to live on earth. When the Apostle Paul was talking he said *"for we shall all appear before the judgment seat of Christ". 2 Corinthians 5:10.*

"We" means all including the speaker (Paul) that is to say all Christians; the Corinthian church members included shall face judgment as well as the unbelievers. *"For the time is come that judgment must begin at the house of God and if it first begin at of us, what shall the end of them that obey not the gospel of God?" 1 peter 4:17*

Judgment is for both those who obeyed God's word to be rewarded and those who disobeyed God's word to be punished at the last day. It is for those who are dead and those who alive. *"And the sea gave us the dead which were in it; and death and hell delivered up the dead which were in them; and they were judged every man according to their work". Rev. 20:12.*

Every human being shall appear before Christ Jesus at the white throne judgment according to the Holy Bible. *"And I saw the great white throne and him that sat on it from whose face the earth and the heaven fled away; and there was found no place for them". Revelation 20:11.* In this judgment everything including physical, natural, fleshly and spiritual beings were present before God.

This is to say that the devil also was present for God's judgment. *"And the devil that deceived them was cast into the lake of fire and brimstone, where the beast and the false prophet are and shall be tormented day and might forever and ever". Rev. 20:10.* Basically those who face judgment are the Christians, the unbelievers, every soul and all demons including the devil and the fallen angels.

On the judgment day no one will escape. *"I charge thee therefore before God and the Lord Jesus Christ who shall judge the quick (living) and the dead at his appearing and his kingdom" 2 Timothy 4:1*

CHAPTER 12

THE JUDGMENT SEAT

"And I saw the great white throne, and him that sat on it, from whose face the earth and heaven fled away; and there was found no place for them". Revelation 20:11.

The seat of judgment is where Christ is seated at the Day of Judgment to judge all flesh, all spirits, all angels and the devil as well. The seat is a white throne in the heavens. The white is a significance of righteousness and the justice manner of the judgment. There is going to be a fair, just and righteous judgment on that day.

The whole world including the inhabitants of the earth and the heavens shall all appear before the judgment seat of God at the day of the judgment. There will be no place for escape on that day for those who are running away from judgment. We shall all be summoned to the seat of judgment under God's arrangement.

"But why dost thou judge thy brother? Or why dost thou set at—-—thy brother? For we shall all stand before the judgment seat of Christ." Romans 14:10 In every law court, there is always a seat reserved or made specifically for the judge to sit on and give judgment. Anyone who sit on that seat has the authority of judgment.

Hence, anyone on the judgment seat is regarded as the judge, and for that they have the authority to execute any deserving judgment to an accused person. We are all accused of the sin by the devil who is also called the accuser of the brethren. *"...for the accuser of our brethren is las down, which accused them before our God day and night" Revelation 12:10.*

At the judgment seat what can justify a soul is the blood of Jesus Christ and that can only be for the believer in Christ Jesus. *"And they overcame him by the blood of the lambs and by the word of their testimony; and they loved not their testimony and they loved not their lives unto the dead" Revelation 12:11.* Jesus Christ gave us victory in the word and the blood. Why Jesus is qualified to sit on the seat of judgment is because He is the atonement of our sins. *"...And if any man sin, we have an advocate with the father, Jesus Christ the righteous. And he is the propitiation for our sins; and not for ours only but also for the sins of the whole world" 1 John 2:1-2.*

CHAPTER 13:
THE VERDICT

"And whosoever was not found written in the book of life was cast into the Lake of fire." Revelation 20:15

The verdict for the sinner at the judgment is categorically state and is a death penalty as the scriptures confirm. *"For the wages of sin is death, but the gift of God is eternal life through Jesus Christ our Lord." Romans 6:23.* This type of death as explained in scripture is the condemnation to eternal hell fire. *"And death and hell were cast into the lake of fire. This is the second death" Rev. 20:14.*

The certainty of the verdict is that it is already stated in scripture even before the judgment day, so that God could be justified in His judgment. *"He that believeth on him is not condemned; but he that believeth not is condemned already, because he hath not believed in the name of the only begotten son of God." John 3: 18.* Those who do not believe are condemned already for the sin of unbelief in the savior, Christ Jesus (Yahshua).

Once a person rejects Christ a verdict is already given against that soul because he did not believe in God's only begotten son. *"And this is the condemnation, that light is come into the world, and men loved darkness rather than light, because their deeds were evil" John 3:19.* The certified reason why people reject Christ is because he is a light and people prefer darkness because of evil deeds.

That is why the verdict of eternal condemnation is given against the soul. *"But the fearful, and unbelieving, and the abominable, and murderers and whoremongers, and sorcerers, and idolaters, and all liars, shall have their part in the Lake which burneth with fire and brimstone which is the second death." Revelation 21:8.* The verdict is already given against all sinful behaviors that people do and the punishment is to be cast unto the Lake of fire.

On the judgment day Jesus Christ (Yahshua) will only sit on the white throne seat to execute the verdict already given in the word of God. *"He that rejecteth me, and receiveth not my words, hath one that judgeth him; the word that I have spoken, the same shall judge him in the last day" John 12:48.*

CHAPTER 14:
VINDICATED BY GRACE

"Even when we were dead in sins, hath quickened us together with Christ, (by grace ye are saved ;)" Ephesians 2:5

The fact that Christ died for us is the grace that vindicates the believer. We were already condemned for destruction under our sinful nature. However, because we have believed in our Lord Jesus and have given our lives over to him, there is no place for condemnation for the believer. *"There is therefore now no condemnation to them which are in Christ Jesus, who walk not after the flesh but after the spirit". Romans 8:1.*

The Lord Jesus Christ took our place of condemnation by dying for the sinner on the cross. *"Who our self-bare our sins in his own body on the tree, that we, being dead to sins, should live unto righteousness by whose stripes ye were healed". 1 Peter 2:24* Christ Jesus has already paid the price for our redemption and salvation by carrying our sins, that is to say he faced the consequence of our sinful behavior.

That is the reason we are vindicated by grace at the Day of Judgment for the simple that we believe in Christ. *"For God sent not his son into the world to condemn the world; but that the world through him might be saved". John 3:17.* Jesus Christ has done the finished work of salvation for the whole world. But it is only accomplished on the platform of faith in Christ Jesus. That is the reason it is by grace we are justified at the Day of Judgment.

"But he was wounded for our transgressions; he was bruised for our iniquities; the chastisement of our peace was upon him, and with his stripes we are healed. Isaiah 53:5 Jesus Christ Has Really been brutalized and punished because of our sinful deeds that is the reason he is able to save us under grace. Christ is therefore God's gracious gift to the world against the day of judgment.

"And not as it was by one that sinned so is the gift; for the judgment was by one to condemnation, but the free gift is many offences unto justification". Romans 5:16. The believer in Christ Jesus is therefore justified in the Day of Judgment.

CHAPTER 15 :
THE DOCTRINE OF BALAAM

"But I have a few things against thee ,because thou hast there those that hold the doctrine of Balaam ,who taught Balak to cast a stumbling

block before the children of Israel, to eat things sacrificed unto idols, and to commit fornication. " Revelations 2:14

The doctrine of Balaam is the strategy that Balaam taught the king of Moab. This doctrine teaches that the Israelites are righteous before God ,therefore they cannot be cursed in any way. So he taught the king of Moab, Balak to seduce the children of Israel to commit fornication with the Moabites and also introduced them to eat meat sacrificed to idols. In this way they become defiled and therefore they shall loose God's protection and glory.

" He hath not beheld iniquity in Jacob ,neither hath he seen perverseness in Israel. The Lord his God is with him, and the shout of a king is among them ." Numbers 23 : 21 Balaam is telling the king of Moab, Balak that, so long as there is no sin ,iniquity or sexual perversion (fornication) in the people of Isreal he cannot curse them ,but instead he blessed them.

So the scriptures further explained the doctrine of Balaam in the book of Numbers 31:16 *" Behold, these caused the children of Israel, through the counsel of Balaam, to commit trespass against the LORD in the matter of Peor, and there was a plague among the congregation of the LORD."* In this portion of scripture it is described as *" the counsel of Balaam "*

So the doctrine of Balaam in our days is the seduction and convincing that the children of God can sin and nothing will happen to them. So they teach that we are under grace ,it doesn't matter if we sin ,because we are covered by the grace of God.

This is a lie and a typical doctrine of Balaam that the enemy is using to lure God's children into fornication, adultery and all forms of sin ,so that the devil can have access to destroy human lives .True grace of God delivers people from sinful life and teaches us to live a godly life.

" For the grace of God that bringeth salvation hath appeared to all men .Teaching us that, denying ungodliness and worldly lust, we should live soberly, righteously and godly, in this present world. " Titus 2:11-12 The reality here is that when you receive grace, it teaches , enables and helps you to overcome lust ,ungodliness and sin as a whole. Again the grace helps you to live a righteous and godly life.

In this 3rd time the doctrine of Balaam is being taught undercover of grace ,some teach that our sins doesn't matter, because we have grace and this has made many children of God fall into all forms of sinful indulgence even in the house of God. Many Christians who are deceived by this doctrine of Balaam are living in sin and yet going to church every Sunday without remorse. That is why many church buildings are full of people who are still living in sins .

CHAPTER 16 :
CORE VALUES OF PEOPLE

" ...Thou art careful and troubled about many things. ..But one thing is needful, and Mary hath chosen that good part ." Luke 10:41-42

There are some things human beings value on earth, those are the things that get their attention the most. What you value most in life is what you invest your time, energy, money and passion on .There are three main core values in life ,these are what people value most ; money, love and entertainment. Money has been the number one core value of most people, to the extent they can even kill for money, lie for money, dupe for money and do anything evil for money.

That is the word of God cautions us against the love of money which brings the most evil. *" For the love of money is the root of all evil : which while some coveted after, they have erred from the faith, pierced themselves through with many sorrows. " 1 Timothy 6:10* The people who see money as their core value tend to love money more than anything in the world. One of the core values is love ,which comprises relationships, marriage and sex .Those who value these things can go to all length to have a lover or to please a lover .

God always warn us in his word against loving and valuing the things of the world.*"Love not the world, neither the things that are in the world, If any man loves the world, the love of the Father is not in him. For all that is in the world, the lust of the flesh, and the lust of the eyes, and the pride of life, is not of the Father, but is of the world. " 1 John 2:15-16*

Those who value love ,relationships, marriage or sex above the word of God will always end up committing sin .Because most at times they are controlled by lust of the flesh, so they end up committing sin.

One core value of people in general is entertainment of all kinds, such as football, movies ,parties ,clubs ,social gatherings and all forms of games. That is why some Christians may not go to church on Sunday, but instead go to movie theaters or game centers ,just to watch football or movies. What God wants us to value is the word of God, like Mary who valued the teachings of Christ and spent all her time listening to the word of God. *"And she had a sister called Mary ,who also sat at Jesus feet and heard his word. "Luke 10 : 39*

CHAPTER 17:
WHAT IS YOUR NAME

" So He said, what is your name ? He said, Jacob " Genesis 32 :27

Your name is the first hand information a person gets about you ,to know who you are. A person's name defines the destiny of the person. In the bible we discover that God gives names to promise to describe their mission on earth. As your name is ,so are you, " *...for as his name is, so is he ,Nabal is his name, and folly is with him ..." 1 Samuel 25 : 25* Nabal probably means a fool and that actually was the character of this man .

The angel ask Jacob what is your name, Jacob means a supplanter, (or deceiver) thus he lived a life of deception, *" And he said, Is not he rightly named Jacob? for he has supplanted me these two times : he took away my birthright; and behold, now he hath taken away my blessing...? Genesis 27:36*

Your name brings with it your destiny, that is why you must know what your name stands for. It was said of the saviour, *" And she shall bring forth a son ,and thou shalt call his name Jesus, for he shall save his people from their sins " Matthew 1:21*

The name Jesus (Yeshua in Hebrew) means a God who is our salvation, thus the mission of Jesus was described in his name. Another name given to Christ further explains his deity " *Behold, a virgin shall be with a child, and shall call his name Emmanuel, which be interpreted is ,God with us ." Matthew 1:23* This name emphasize the fact that Jesus Christ is Lord and God Almighty. Your name can have a positive or negative effect in your life as a Christian.

That is why a change of name is possible at times, Jacob was changed to Israel (a prince with God) Genesis 32 : 28 Abram was changed to Abraham (a father of nations) *"Neither shall thy name any more be called Abram, but thy name shall be Abraham, for a father of many nations have I made thee ." Genesis 17:5* We discover that Abraham started having the promised children when his name was changed.

Jabez also had a similar experience *" And Jabez was more honourable than his brethren : and his mother called his name Jabez, saying, because I bare him with sorrow. And Jabez called on the God of Isreal, saying Oh that thou wouldest bless me indeed and enlarge my coast, and that thine hand might be with me, and that thou wouldest keep me from evil, that it may not grieve me ? And God granted him that which he requested. " 1 Chronicles 4 : 9-10*

CHAPTER 18 :
THE CHILDREN OF THE KINGDOM

" The field is the world, the good seeds are the children of the kingdom, but the tares are the children of the wicked one. " Matthew 13 : 38

The children of the kingdom are those who have accepted the Lord Jesus Christ as their saviour. They have come to accept the Lord Jesus Christ, and are born-again and spirit filled. The children of the kingdom are those who are pursuing the eternal life in God's kingdom. They are led by the spirit of God, and for that matter they have come to recognise the voice of God. *" For as many as are led by the spirit of God, they are the sons of God. " Romans 8:14*

The children of the kingdom are those who are separated from the life of sin." *Wherefore come out from among them, and be ye separate, saith the Lord, and touch not the unclean thing :and I will receive you. And I will be a father unto you, and ye shall be my sons and daughters ,saith the Lord Almighty.* " *2 Corinthians 6 : 17-18* The children of the kingdom are those who are consecrated in their heart and have decided to abstain from all forms of sinful appearance.

God receives us as his children if we forgo all the sinful ways of the world. For instance the apostle John cautions, " *Love not the world, neither the things that are in the world. If any man love the world, the love of the Father is not in him .For all that is in the world, the lust of the flesh, and the lust of the eyes, and the pride of life oise not of the Father, but is of the world.* " *1 John 2:15-16* Those who are the children of the kingdom are suppose to only live the Lord and not the sinful world of lust, and pride which destroys sinners.

The children of the kingdom are those who are delivered from the powers of darkness. *"who hath delivered us from the power of darkness, and hath translated us into the kingdom of his dear son ." Colossians 1:13* The children of the kingdom are heavenly minded and focus on things, above. *" If ye then be risen with Christ, seek those things which are above, where Christ sitteth on the right hand of God. Set your affection on things above., and not on things on the earth. " Colossians 3 : 1-2*

CHAPTER 19 :
THE MANIFESTED LIFE

" For the life was manifested, and we have seen it, and bear witness, and shew unto you that eternal life, which was with the father and was manifested unto us. " 1 John 1 : 2

The Manifested life is the life of the father in heaven, it is the life that was hidden from us due to our sins. God forbid human beings from eating the tree of life ,that could have given us everlasting life way back in the garden of Eden.

" And the Lord God said, behold, the man is become as one of us , to know good and evil, and now, lest he put forth his hand and take also of the tree of life and eat and live forever. Therefore the Lord God sent him forth from the garden of Eden, to till the ground from whence he was taken. " Genesis 3: 22-23

God drove Adam and Eve from the garden of Eden on purpose, so that they will not see the tree of life nor eat of it ." *So he drove out the man ,and placed at the east of the garden of Eden Cherubims, and a flaming sword which turned every way mot keep the way of the tree of life. " Genesis 3: 24* ,Thus ,God took the human being from everlasting life so that no man had the chance of living forever. The everlasting life that was in the tree of life was hidden from us .

Jesus Christ ,however came as the manifested life for us who desire to have this everlasting life to discover it Jesus himself said among other things that he is the bread of life, the resurrection and the life. *" Verily, verily, I say unto you, He that believeth on me hath everlasting life. I am that bread of life. " John 6:47-48*

Jesus came as a manifested life, which was hidden from human beings for ages ,because of sin .The words of Jesus all proved that he is the manifested life.

" I am the living bread which came down from heaven, if any man eat of this bread, he shall live forever, and the bread that I give is my flesh ,which I will give for the life of the world. " John 6: 51 Jesus Christ always revealed himself as the life of God from heaven for humanity to partake of and enjoy the father's life forever. Jesus' life is a life for all to live with, the dead and the living alike.

"Jesus said unto her, I am the resurrection, and the life, he that believeth in me though he were dead, yet shall he live. And whosoever liveth and believeth in me shall never die ,Believest thou this. ? " John 11:25-26 Jesus Christ, therefore is our manifested life that God has given back to all human beings.

CHAPTER 20:
THE WAY TO HEAVEN

" Jesus saith unto, I am the way, the truth, and the life, no man cometh unto the father but by me " John 14:6

The way to heaven is on the cross of Calvary, Jesus Christ came as the way to heaven, no wonder he said, " I am the way " The way to heaven is only found in Jesus Christ of Nazareth, it is the way of righteousness, it is the way of the cross and it is also described as the narrow way. *" Because strait is the gate and narrow is the way which leadeth unto life and few there be that find it " Matthew 7:14*

The way to heaven is the narrow way that only a few who are willing to loose so much weight in order to enter this narrow way can enter . On the narrow way to heaven is only a life of righteousness where obedience to the word of God is enforced. On this way to heaven no sinful activity is permitted. *"And there shall in no wise enter into it anything that defileth, neither whatever worketh abomination or maketh a lie ,but they which are written in the lamb's book of life. " Revelations 21:27*

The way to heaven is the way of purity, the only people who are liable to enter are the ones who are living a life of righteousness. The way to hear is not meant for those who commit iniquity, Jesus emphasized this, *" Not everyone that saith unto me ,Lord, Lord, shall enter into the kingdom of heaven, but he that doeth the will of my father which is in heaven. Many will say to me in that day, Lord, Lord, have we not prophesied in thy name? And in thy name cast out devils ? and in thy name done many wonderful works .And then will I profess unto them, I never knew you, depart from me ,ye that work iniquity, " Matthew 7: 21-23*

The way to heaven is the way of the righteous, and not the way of the hypocrites. The aforementioned portion of scripture explains that some people would be denied entrance to the kingdom of heaven because of their lifestyle of iniquities. The way to the kingdom of heaven, is the way of commitment where the body is a sacrifice to God .

"I beseech you therefore, brethren , by the mercies of God ,that ye present your bodies as a living sacrifice ,holy ,acceptable,unto God, which is your reasonable service .And be not conformed tho this world, but be ye transformed by the renewing of your mind, that ye may prove what is that good, and acceptable, and perfect will of God ." Romans 12:2

CHAPTER 21: THE GOD KIND OF FAITH

" For the life was manifested, and we have seen it, and bear witness, and shew unto you that eternal life, which was with the father and was manifested unto us. " 1 John 1:2

The God kind of life is the only life that defines the immortality of God. The God kind of life is the life referred to us as eternal life which only God gives his children. It is the life that Jesus Christ came to manifest to the whole world. Before Jesus Christ came, this life was hidden with the father and only God had that life. It is the life that knows no beginning nor ending, it is the kind of life described in Revelations 1:8

Jesus describes the life of God in full detail in this portion of scripture ; Alpha and Omega.that is A and Z ,this means God begins and ends every life, but he has no beginning nor ending. The next phrase is the " the beginning and the ending " which also implies that God's life begins every other life and the same ends every other life. In reality God determines life, it's beginning and it's ending.

Another phrase that describes the God kind of life is *"which is, which was and which is to come. "* Here it is emphasizing a God who entails the past of life and things. The present life which is, and God is also a God who knows and controls the future, *"which is to come "*

This means God's life is from everlasting to everlasting, from generation to generation and from age to age .It is a perpetual life, unabated and continual. Jesus describes this life in another scripture as resurrection and the life. *"Jesus said unto her ,I am the resurrection, and the life , he that believeth in me though he were dead, yet shall he live." John 11:25*

The resurrection means it is reviving life, it quickens or gives life to people or the dead .Jesus manifested the life of God, therefore he is the life ." *But is now made manifest by the appearing of our saviour Jesus Christ ,who hath abolished death, and hath brought life and immortality to light through the gospel, Timothy 1 :10*

The God kind y life abolishes death, the death of going to hell fire. (Revelations 20:14-15)Jesus came to establish immortality with the people of God who believe in him .

CHAPTER : 22

THE LIFE OF GOD

" (For the life was manifested, and we have seen it, and bear witness, and shew unto you that eternal life, which was with the Father, and was manifested unto us;) " 1 John 1:2

The Life of God is an eternal lfe ,the life that only God had before Christ came . This life is the one that knows no end and it doesn't have a beginning , it is a perpetual life and only God had that nature of life . The life of God is the one that knows no negativity , , omen , calamity , no pain , npo sorrows , no death , no sickness , etc. *" And God shall wipe away all tears from their eyes and there shall be no more death , neither sorrow , nor crying , neither shall there be any more pain , for the former things are passed away ." Rev. 21:4*

This kind of life is what God intends for us human beings to partake . God wanted to impart every human being with this life of God that is full of bliss and without any side effect nor evil occurrence. Can you imagine living a life where nothing happens to make you sad ,cry ,shed tears, nor bring pain to you . This is the life of God that is established in heaven and the paradise of God .This is the life that God gave Adam and Eve in the garden of Eden , before the devil set in and destroyed everything .

The life of God is a life that knows no defeat , disappointment ,nor failure ,because God is over all and conquers all . Above all God made everything to work well and together for the advantage and the good of his purpose for our lives . Why we fall short of the life of God is because we live in a different atmosphere , either than where God originally placed us . Our sinful style has misplaced us from the kingdom of God and now we live in the rheam of darkness where satan has his seat of evil in our heart . " For behold darkness shall cover the earth , and gross darkness the people , but the Lord shall arise upon thee , and his glory shall be seen upon thee ." Isaiah 60:2

The life of God is the one of light , where sin cannot dwell , because the light of God's word dispels darkness and the light describes the way of righteousness for us all . " For everyone that doeth evil; hateth the light , neither cometh to the light , lest his deeds should be reproved . But he that doeth truth cometh to the light , that his deeds may be made manifest that they are wrought in God " John 3:20-21 The light of God has the characteristics of righteousness and good deeds .

CHAPTER 23 :
THE ORIGIN OF LIFE

" Let that day be darkness; let not God regard it from above, neither let the light shine upon it." Job 3:4

The origin of life is God , the Lord made life out of his breath for every living thing to have life . This is the more reason , , there is no real life , whenever we are disconnected from God who is our source of life . God created life for us out of his word , and the breath that came out of God into our nostrils made us alive out of dust . Without the breath of Almighty God, we are all dust of the ground .

" And the Lord God formed man of the dust of the ground, and breathed into his nostrils the breath of life; and man became a living soul." Genesis 2:7

God made us out of the clay , so were are like statue , a non-living thing until God breathed his breath that gave us life through our nostrils .The breath became the life giving spirit , that was given to us as his children and creation . God wanted us to share in his divinity ,that is why he gave us life by his breath . God is a spirit and that spirit was imparted into the lifeless clay so man become a living being {spirit } that resides in the dust .

The composite of man is the dust of the ground and the spirit of God .When a person dies the dust is detached from the spirit , the spirit departs from the dust {body} ." Then shall the dust return to the earth as it was: and the spirit shall return unto God who gave it" Ecclesiastes 12:7 The spirit that returns to God after death is called the soul .The soul returns to God because that is where it came from . The soul is connected to the spirit , the soul here is responsible for all the senses of the human being including , hearing , smelling , talking , seeing , feeling and every attribute that shows life .

" And the very God of peace sanctify you wholly; and I pray God your whole spirit and soul and body be preserved blameless unto the coming of our Lord Jesus Christ." 1 Thessalonians 5:23 God wanted us to live in sanctity , purity, and righteously in his sight as the handiwork of God . To live a blameless life from sin and defilement . God created humans as his mirror image on earth ,so that we will live a godly life in this world . *"And the Lord God formed man of the dust of the ground, and breathed into his nostrils the breath of life; and man became a living soul." Genesis 2:7* So God is the origin of life for every living soul that has breath .

CHAPTER 24 : THE TREE OF LIFE

" *And out of the ground made the Lord God to grow every tree that is pleasant to the sight, and good for food; the tree of life also in the midst of the garden, and the tree of knowledge of good and evil.* "**Genesis 2:9**

The tree of life is the plant that God planted in the garden of Eden , so that it will sustain human life on earth , provided we eat it . The tree of life was a good and edible fruit that was meant to bring long life to everyone who eats it .The tree of life was not really pointed out to Adam , although they could see it , they had no idea what this tree of life would do for them if they ate it . God rather forbid them from eating the tree of knowledge of good and evil . " *And the Lord God commanded the man , saying of every tree of the garden , thou mayest freely eat " Genesis 2:16* The scriptures made it clear that God wanted Adam and his wife to eat the tree of life also , so that they would live forever .

Instead they choose to eat the forbidden fruits , " *But of the tree of the knowledge of good and evil, thou shalt not eat of it: for in the day that thou eatest thereof thou shalt surely die." Genesis 2:17* This forbidden fruit had death in it , although it gives knowledge of good and evil to everyone who eats of it . God wanted humans to live forever and not die , that is why God forbid him from eating this tree that brings death.God's original intention was that the man and his wife would eat the tree of life and live forever on earth .

However , God wanted us to live innocently without sin ,that is why God forbids man from eating the tree that gives knowledge of good and evil . Because with that knowledge one will choose to do evil anytime he wishes . So when man finally rushed to eat this tree that brings death instead of eating the tree of life . God had to do something to stop them from eating the tree of life . This was necessary because man could have eaten and lived forever doing evil , because he has the knowledge to do it .

" And the Lord God said, Behold, the man is become as one of us, to know good and evil: and now, lest he put forth his hand, and take also of the tree of life, and eat, and live for ever:23 [1]Therefore the Lord God sent him forth from the garden of Eden, to till the ground from whence he was taken.24 [2]So he drove out the man; and he placed at the east of the garden of Eden Cherubims, and a flaming sword which turned every way, to keep the way of the tree of life." Genesis 3:22-24

---

1. *https://www.holybible.com/gen.3.23*

2. *https://www.holybible.com/gen.3.24*

CHAPTER 25: THE DISOBEDIENCE

" But of the tree of the knowledge of good and evil, thou shalt not eat of it: for in the day that thou eatest thereof thou shalt surely die. " Genesis 2:17

The disobedience of Adam was the downfall of every human being on earth . The Lord gave us a continual life , but it was based on the condition of obedience to the commandment of God . God emphatically said , *" for in the day that thou eatest thereof thou shalt surely die. "* So death was the consequence of disobedience to the word of God . God's plan for humanity was altered the moment they disobeyed God and started living in sin .

Satan knew that the only way he could destroy human life is to make sure that man will disobey God . The devil came in his subtil and cunning way and deceived them to disobey God , and now the aftermath effect is death . The devil tricked Eve when said *" ye shall not surely die " Genesis 3:4* The devil promises a better life that people will enjoy by disobeying God's word . *" For God doth know that in the day ye eat thereof, then your eyes shall be opened, and ye shall be as gods, knowing good and evil." Genesis 3:5*

The devil deceived Eve to desire to be like God , to know the difference between good and evil ; making it seem like God was hiding something from them . God wants us to have the best of life , yet he does not enforce his will on us . God gives us the option to choose between obeying God's word or disobeying it . The devil influences our choice and daily decisions in a negative way , making us disobey God through his deception ,no wonder he is called the deceiver .

" *And the great dragon was cast out, that old serpent, called the Devil, and Satan, which deceiveth the whole world: he was cast out into the earth, and his angels were cast out with him.*" *Revelation 12:9* The devil has the animal nature of a serpent , here the old serpent refers to the one in the garden of Eden who deceived Adam and Eve . Because of the disobedience God now pronounced the death sentence over humanity .

"*In the sweat of thy face shalt thou eat bread, till thou return unto the ground; for out of it wast thou taken: for dust thou art, and unto dust shalt thou return.* ." *Genesis 3:19* The disobedience brought so much evil , calamity , pain , sickness , sweat , hard labour , disasters , etc. to human life . God wants us to enjoy a perpetual and unabated life , but on the platform of obedience .

CHAPTER 26: IGNORING THE TREE OF LIFE

"And out of the ground made the Lord God to grow every tree that is pleasant to the sight, and good for food; the tree of life also in the midst of the garden, and the tree of knowledge of good and evil. " Genesis 2:9

Adam and Eve ignored the tree of life ,the very tree that God actually wanted them to eat and live forever . Why they ignored the tree of life is because their focus was on the forbidden fruit instead of all the multitudes of fruits in the garden of Eden.There are a variety of fruits , so many and even unaccountable including the tree of life . All these fruits were edible and edible and pleasant to the eyes , yet Adam and Eve rushed to disobey God by eating the tree of knowledge of good and evil .

They ignored the tree of life because of a number of reasons , the first reason is that they were ignorant of the fact that the very tree will give them life . Their ignorance was because they choose to listen to deception of the devil . The scriptures declare ,

"My people are destroyed for lack of knowledge: because thou hast rejected knowledge, I will also reject thee, that thou shalt be no priest to me: seeing thou hast forgotten the law of thy God, I will also forget thy children." Hosea 4:6 At times we ignore the truth of scripture and follow deception of ideology , fantasy ,illusion and philosophy that comes from the satanic deception .

"Now the Spirit speaketh expressly, that in the latter times some shall depart from the faith, giving heed to seducing spirits, and doctrines of devils;" 1 Timothy 4:1 There are so many doctrines of the devil , that are spreading so fast , making so many of God's children go astray from the path of righteousness and are living in sin . Even as Adam and Eve ignored the tree of life , we can also ignore our tree of life which is the salvation that we have in Christ Jesus .

By living a sinful life and making it a standard of living is the way of destruction. Because we found out that God later had to stop the man from eating the tree of life , because he choose to eat the tree of death { Knowledge of good and evil } .

"Woe unto them that call evil good, and good evil; that put darkness for light, and light for darkness; that put bitter for sweet, and sweet for bitter!21 [1]Woe unto them that are wise in their own eyes, and prudent in their own sight! " Isaiah 5:20-22 When people choose a sinful lifestyle as a standard , and even justify their sinful behaviour calling it a good and acceptable lifestyle they loose the life of God and the salvation of Yeshua our Lord .

1. *https://www.holybible.com/isa.5.21*

CHAPTER 27 :
THE DECEPTION OF THE DEVIL

"And the great dragon was cast out, that old serpent, called the Devil, and Satan, which deceiveth the whole world: he was cast out into the earth, and his angels were cast out with him. " Revelation 12:9

The devil is known to be a deceiver who deceives the nations ; the whole world with his lies and flatteries . The devil uses a very subtil and cunning wisdom to imagine , scheme , plan and do evil . The subtil nature is the strategic way of doing evil so as to outwit or trick the victim . *"Now the serpent was more subtil than any beast of the field which the Lord God had made. And he said unto the woman, Yea, hath God said, Ye shall not eat of every tree of the garden? " Genesis 3:1*

The devil used the body of the serpent to achieve his work of deception , that is how the devil usually operates through bodies , animal or human bodies . The devils medium of deception has always been human beings ,especially now that human beings have become many . In the garden of Eden there were no other human beings apart from Adam and Eve , that is the more reason why the devil used the body of the serpent . The medium of deception the devil uses are material possessions ; lack of it , or much of it . The devil can capitalize on your lack of material provisions to deceive you .

For instance Yeshua talks about the deceitfulness of wealth , *"He also that received seed among the thorns is he that heareth the word; and the care of this world, and the deceitfulness of riches, choke the word, and he becometh unfruitful." Matthew 13:22* Thedevil can use money to deceive you in such a way that you will forget God and the money will become your God . You will do things because you have the money to do , whether God's word permits it or not .

You may choose to listen to the voice of money instead of the voice of God's word for your life .In the parable of the *"rich fool"* we discover that this rich man was deceived by money to think that, so long as he has the money or food to eat , his soul will enjoy long life . {Luke 12:16-21} *"But God said unto him, Thou fool, this night thy soul shall be required of thee: then whose shall those things be, which thou hast provided?" Luke 12:20* The devil deceived the nations with so much magic powers to seduce and deceive even the very elect of God , through the miracles that false prophets perform false teachers who teach false doctrine to lead the body of Christ astray from the path of righteousness .

"And many false prophets shall rise, and shall deceive many ." Matthew 24:11

"For many shall come in my name, saying, I am Christ; and shall deceive many." Matthew 24:5

"For there shall arise false Christs, and false prophets, and shall shew great signs and wonders; insomuch that, if it were possible, they shall deceive the very elect." Matthew 24:24

The deception of the devil is to make sure we all do evil without knowing it . The ministry of the false prophets is that they cover up sin to the extent that their congregations do not fear to commit sin . Because they don't preach about righteousness , neither do they preach against sin .

CHAPTER 28 :
THE LIFE OF HUMAN BEINGS

"And seekest thou great things for thyself? seek them not: for, behold, I will bring evil upon all flesh, saith the Lord: but thy life will I give unto thee for a prey in all places

whither thou goest. "Jeremiah 45:5

The life that God gave us was meant to be a life to live to the fulfillment of God's will . Among other things we were created in the image of God , so that we can do what God created us to do as people of God .The life of the human was to honour God , by displaying the image of God as God's children in a godly character . God's idea of human life was supposed to be submitted and a humble life to God Almighty .

" For we are his workmanship, created in Christ Jesus unto good works, which God hath before ordained that we should walk in them. " Ephesians 2:10 The human life was God's ordinance for us to live up to expectation , the Lord created a godly and righteous life for us to live and walk in them . Human life was meant to do good works and good deeds .God wanted us to know him and serve him as creator in a submissive way .

This was supposed to be a life of obedience that produces innocence like that of a baby . The human life was supposed to be controlled and directed by the word of God .We are made to survive by obeying the word of God . *"But he answered and said, It is written, Man shall not live by bread alone, but by every word that proceedeth out of the mouth of God. "| Matthew 4:4* Jesus gave the devil this reply after the devil had tempted him to disobey God , by turning stone into bread .

This shows how important it is that we should know the word of God and live to obey it all the days of our lives . In this scripture it is also clear that we can only enjoy God's life he meant for us to live by knowing and obeying the word of God for our lives ." *live by the word* " actually means you can live long , so long as you obey the word of God . The life of the human being is best sustained by the word of God .

The sincerest desire of God for us is that we live long and enjoy God's salvation for mankind ." *With long life will I satisfy him, and shew him my salvation.* " *Psalm 91:16* Living long without salvation of your soul is a wasted life , because at the end you loose your soul in hell fire . The salvation of the soul is a matter of making Jesus your Lord and saviour , by obeying the word of God and submitting to God's salvation ." *For what is a man advantaged, if he gain the whole world, and lose himself, or be cast away?* " *Luke 10:25*

CHAPTER 29:
THE LIFE SPINE OF HUMANITY

"And the Lord said, My spirit shall not always strive with man, for that he also is flesh: yet his days shall be an hundred and twenty years. "Genesis 6:3

God's decision to discontinue the life life spine of human beings was prompted by our sinful character . God said his " *spirit shall not always strive with man* " This means God will not allow the life-giving spirit that is in man to continue in his flesh . The life giving spirit that came from the breath of the Almighty is the soul within human beings without which there is no life .

" *And God made the firmament, and divided the waters which were under the firmament from the waters which were above the firmament: and it was so." Genesis 2:7* God's original intention was to allow his spirit of life to abide in our flesh forever . However , the human flesh became so sinful that God was not comfortable with it . Anytime human beings do evil , the spirit of God is grieved within us , to the extent God could not tolerate it any longer .

" And God saw that the wickedness of man *was* great in the earth, and *that* every imagination of the thoughts of his heart *was* only evil continually.

6 [1]And it repented the Lord that he had made man on the earth, and it grieved him at his heart." Genesis 6:5-6 Thus , God decided to reduce the life spine of human beings from one hundred years upwards to one hundred and twenty years at most .

---

1. https://www.holybible.com/gen.6.6

This however continued for a while and God had to reduce the life spine again because of the sinful rate of mankind , which became increasingly worse .God finally reduced it to seventy years or at most eight years of a life spine . *" For all our days are passed away in thy wrath: we spend our years as a tale that is told.10 [2]The days of our years are threescore years and ten; and if by reason of strength they be fourscore years, yet is their strength labour and sorrow; for it is soon cut off, and we fly away. " Psalm 90:9-10*

A score is twenty , so threescore is sixty , and fourscore is eighty . God was being generous to us by giving us such number of years to fulfill , because our sins became too grievous for God to endure seeing our life in us . So God's decision became firm , that after the spirit of life has tarried with us for a while , it will depart to God again . *" Then shall the dust return to the earth as it was: and the spirit shall return unto God who gave it." Ecclesiastes 12:7*

2. *https://www.holybible.com/psa.90.10*

CHAPTER 30 : NUMBERING YOUR DAYS

" So teach us to number our days, that we may apply our hearts unto wisdom. " Psalm 90:12

Numbering your days is a matter of adding more years to your life spine or vice versa . A person can add a number of days to their lifestyle depending on his or her lifestyle . Whenever we do good , we are actually prolonging our life spine on earth . Conversely whenever we do evil , we shorten our life spine in the process . Most at times the number of years God wants us to fulfil is dependent on our good deeds or our evil deeds .

When a person knows how to number his days , he or she understands that living long is dependant to a large extent on our character . For instance the command to honour parent came with a promise of long life . " *Children, obey your parents in the Lord: for this is right.2 [1]Honour thy father and mother; (which is the first commandment with promise;)3 [2]That it may be well with thee, and thou mayest live long on the earth. " Ephesians 6:1-3* In this portion of scripture it is very clear that if a person honours and obeys parents in the Lord , such a person is guaranteed a long life .

On the other hand any one that disobeys and disrespects his or her parents in the Lord is bound to shorten his or her life spine . In the book of Daniel we notice that Daniel advised a particular king to stop doing evil and start doing good , and that it will be a credit of long life for him . " *Wherefore, O king, let my counsel be*

1. *https://www.holybible.com/eph.6.2*
2. *https://www.holybible.com/eph.6.3*

acceptable unto thee, and break off thy sins by righteousness, and thine iniquities by shewing mercy to the poor; if it may be a lengthening of thy tranquillity." Daniel 4:27

In this scripture there was a condition of long life given to the king , and this is all about a life of righteousness . King Nebuchadnezza was told to stop committing sin and also he had to show mercy to people and stop the life of iniquity . The truth of life is that it feeds on righteousness and obedience to the word of God .All throughout the bible we read the account of so many people who died because of their sins . A typical example is Judas Ischariot who " *...Now this man purchased a field with the reward of iniquity; and falling headlong, he burst asunder in the midst, and all his bowels gushed out." Acts 1:18*

Judas' life was shortened , because of the sin of betrayal , which he did against Jesus when he betrayed him . Another example is the King Belshazzar who sinned very much against the Lord by using golden and silver vessels of God to drink strong drinks and praise the gods of gold and silver .

" *This is the interpretation of the thing: MENE; God hath numbered thy kingdom, and finished it.27 [3]TEKEL; Thou art weighed in the balances, and art found wanting.28 [4]PERES; Thy kingdom is divided, and given to the Medes and Persians.29 [5]Then commanded Belshazzar, and they clothed Daniel with scarlet, and put a chain of gold about his neck, and made a proclamation concerning him, that he should be the third ruler in the kingdom.In that night was Belshazzar the king of the Chaldeans slain." Daniel 5:26-30*

---

3. *https://www.holybible.com/dan.5.27*
4. *https://www.holybible.com/dan.5.28*
5. *https://www.holybible.com/dan.5.29*

In numbering your days , you increase your life spine by living righteous life ; doing the right thing in the sight of God ,by obeying the commandment of God . Sin is the foothole of death .*"O death, where is thy sting? O grave, where is thy victory?56* [6]*The sting of death is sin; and the strength of sin is the law.57* [7]*But thanks be to God, which giveth us the victory through our Lord Jesus Christ. " 1 Corinthians 15:55-57*

---

6. *https://www.holybible.com/1co.15.56*

7. *https://www.holybible.com/1co.15.57*

CHAPTER 31: SATISFIED WITH LIFE

" With long life will I satisfy him, and shew him my salvation." Psalm 91:16

God satisfies his faithful children with longlife , this means the Lord gives them the credit of living long .Life is the food of the soul , the soul survives by feeding on life from God . God promises his beloved children a long life as long as they are committed to loving God .The satisfaction comes after we have met God's condition of long life . We see this in the previous verse " *Because he hath set his love upon me, therefore will I deliver him: I will set him on high, because he hath known my name.15* [1]*He shall call upon me, and I will answer him: I will be with him in trouble; I will deliver him, and honour him." Psalm 91:14-15*

The first condition of long life God stated is " *set his love upon*" God . Whenever you set your love upon God , you become liable to obey God and keep his commandments . The second condition is "call upon me " , this is the aspect of prayer , the person who wants to be satisfied with long life must learn the habit of prayer at all times .Yeshua had to pray to God to help him overcome death in the days of his flesh . " *Who in the days of his flesh, when he had offered up prayers and supplications with strong crying and tears unto him that was able to save him from death, and was heard in that he feared; " Hebrews 5:7*

God satisfies his people with long life when they pray and call upon him . life is a gift from God for us to enjoy , Yeshua said *"The thief cometh not, but for to steal, and to kill, and to destroy:*

---

1. https://www.holybible.com/psa.91.15

I am come that they might have life, and that they might have it more abundantly."John 10:"10 The life that Jesus promised to use to satisfy his children is fullness and abundance of life .This means we enjoy the life now and also the life hereafter . God wants us to have the life of two worlds , the life now and the life eternal .

" For bodily exercise profiteth little: but godliness is profitable unto all things, having promise of the life that now is, and of that which is to come. "1 Timothy 4:8 God satisfies us with long life , that is unabated , a life that continues in eternity .

CHAPTER 32:
Your Own Understanding

" Trust in the Lord with all thine heart; and lean not unto thine own understanding " Proverbs 3:5

Your own understanding is what you think , reason and believe something is ,was and will be like . It is about your own way of seeing things as a human being . This means your point of view of things . The way you see things differ from the way God sees things , the way you figure out things about situations and what is happening in and around you , is " *your own understanding* " In the opening scripture , the word of God tells us to lean not unto our own understanding , but to trust in the Lord .

Your own understanding involves calculations that may arrive at your human solutions . However , God's way of doing things does not depend on our human reasoning or calculations as the prophet Isaiah states *" For my thoughts are not your thoughts, neither are your ways my ways, saith the Lord." Isaiah 55:8* God's thoughts are his resolutions , solutions ,plans , ideas and decisions , which is highly different from your own thoughts and understanding . The scripture further explains in the following verses .

" For as the heavens are higher than the earth, so are my ways higher than your ways, and my thoughts than your thoughts." Isaiah 55:9 God's own understanding is mighty and superior , it is the way of the supernatural and the miraculous . The child of God might see impossibility , yet God's ways are always full of possibilities . Where we lack the capacity God gives us all the strength we need to step out

into the greatness of our destiny . That is why we must learn to trust in God and not our own understanding of things .

" *And he said, The things which are impossible with men are possible with God." Luke 18:27* When we focus on our past experience we tend to loose faith in some situations and begin to imagine how it can fail like what happened before . However , if we have the tenderness to rely on God , then we are sure of the victory through the word of God .

Chapter 33:
What To Learn On

" and lean not unto thine own understanding " Proverbs 3:5

What you lean on determines what you get in life . What happens to you in life is what determines the solution you need .God wants you to lean on him alone , for he alone is your God and your saviour .The Lord is your provider , healer, sx\

Saviour and source of blessings .The Lord alone determines the joys you get in life and the good things that come on your way . It is very important that as a christian you put your trust in the Lord and not in any other thing .

Like the Psalmist said ," *The Lord is my light and my salvation; whom shall I fear? the Lord is the strength of my life; of whom shall I be afraid? " Psalm 27:1* The believer should understand that the enemy is around the corner to destroy human life and for that matter , God is the defender and our deliverer .The child of God must lean on God's unfailing love and his divine strength on our side . " When the wicked, *even* mine enemies and my foes, came upon me to eat up my flesh, they stumbled and fell." Psalm 27:2

The enemy comes on purpose to eat up our flesh , this means the enemy wants to afflict God's children with sickness . But if we trust in God , the devil will stumble and fall down . To lean on the Lord is the best , because he alone has the solution to our predicaments in life . *"Yea, though I walk through the valley of the shadow of death, I will fear no evil: for thou art with me; thy rod and thy staff they comfort me." Psalm 23:4* The rod is a significance of power and the presence of

God , it is also called staff and it is the same staff that God anointed for Moses to use to perform miracles in Egypt.

Why we must lean on the Lord is because in the time of trouble he will hide and protect from all evil ,"*One thing have I desired of the Lord, that will I seek after; that I may dwell in the house of the Lord all the days of my life, to behold the beauty of the Lord, and to enquire in his temple.5* [1]*For in the time of trouble he shall hide me in his pavilion: in the secret of his tabernacle shall he hide me; he shall set me up upon a rock. "Psalm 27:4-5*

1. *https://www.holybible.com/psa.27.5*

CHAPTER 34:
THE SHEEP OF HIS PASTURE

" Know ye that the Lord he is God: it is he that hath made us, and not we ourselves; we are his people, and the sheep of his pasture." Psalm 100:3

To be the sheep of his pasture is to be led by God on a daily basis for our daily bread .The word pasture is the feed for the flocks in general ,so when the scripture declares that we are the sheep of his pasture , it is stating the fact that God daily feeds us with food and all our needs are met by him . When that happens , we have a responsibility to allow the Lord to be our shepherd , so he can successful lead us to greener pastures .

" The Lord is my shepherd; I shall not want." Psalm 23:1 Declares the Psalmist who trusted in God to be a provider for everything that he needs in life ,and he continued to explain the work of the Lord as a shepherd over our lives . " *He maketh me to lie down in green pastures: he leadeth me beside the still waters." Psalm 23:2* God like any good and experienced shepherd leads the sheep to a place of green and flesh pastures , where there could be flesh leaves , grass or any form of pasture for the flock .

Our God always leads us to a place of provision where he is eager to provide for us .What God has told us in his word is to lead us on paths of righteousness ." *He restoreth my soul: he leadeth me in the paths of righteousness for his name's sake." Psalm 23:3* When we are submit to God as humble sheep he gently and tenderly leads us to do the right thing , so that we can have the life of righteousness .

Our Lord Jesus Christ really said that he is a good and trustworthy shepherd , who is ready to even lay down his life for the sheep .

" *I am the good shepherd: the good shepherd giveth his life for the sheep* "*John 10:11* Jesus is our shepherd , and that is the more reason why he died on that cross of calvary to save our life . Jesus realized that in feeding the sheep , we need his blood as part of the pasture , that is why Yeshua shed his blood for us all . " *Then Jesus said unto them, Verily, verily, I say unto you, Except ye eat the flesh of the Son of man, and drink his blood, ye have no life in you* "*John 6:53*

Don't miss out!

Visit the website below and you can sign up to receive emails whenever Ezekiel C. Melchisedec publishes a new book. There's no charge and no obligation.

https://books2read.com/r/B-A-YKXL-HTHNC

BOOKS 2 READ

Connecting independent readers to independent writers.

Did you love *The Apostle's Doctrine*? Then you should read *New Testament Doctrine*[1] by Ezekiel C. Melchisedec!

[2]

Learn doctrines that are relevant in the New Testament bible . In this book chapters and verses are given a detailed expositional approach to the reader . Anyone who wants to study The New Testament Doctrine will find this book as the perfect answer to his or her quest . All the chapters in this book are full of expositions of the New Testament teaching by the Apostles , especially Paul .

" New Testament Doctrine is what governs the body of Christ and Christianity as a whole . This is the more reason why the church must study New Testament teachings . This book is highly

1. https://books2read.com/u/mqBzKe

2. https://books2read.com/u/mqBzKe

recommended for church leaders , pastors , apostles , bible teachers and students alike .

The kingdom is an atmosphere , environment , or rheam where the word of God has the final authority over the hearts of people . Where God's word reigns , where God's people hear the word of God and they obey . It is a kingdom , that is why the bible says the kingdom of God is among you " nor will they say, 'See here!' or 'See there!' For indeed, the kingdom of God is within you." Luke 17 :21

When the word of God is the authority that controls your life , then you have the kingdom of God . The kingdom of God is an environment where people have received God's word and they obey it ."

" Spiritual Understanding

Spiritual understanding , is very important , is about understanding the word of God , understanding prayer , understanding the reason why we do praises , we do worship , understanding baptism , understanding preaching, understanding the cross of our Lord Jesus cross . Understanding heaven , eternity, the second coming of our Lord Jesus Christ .

Not everybody understands spiritual things , some people when we talk about spiritual things , is some kind of foolishness . The bible says in 1 Corinthians , 1:18 " For the preaching of the cross is to them that perish foolishness; but unto us which are saved it is the power of God " At times when we are preaching the word of God becomes foolishness for those who are perishing . When the word of God is foolishness, it means that it has no effect on you . It has no wisdom or knowledge ,it does not make any sense for you . " A quote from the book .

Also by Ezekiel C. Melchisedec

Season Two
Letters From God (Love of God)

Standalone
Discovering Godly Riches
Marriage According To God
The Prophetic Guide
Praying Against Demons
Marriage Pills
The Success Pro
Prophetic Prayer Companion
Prophetic Guide And Prayers
Understanding The Prophetic
New Testament Doctrine
Pastoral Etiquette
Letters From God Devotional
The Apostle's Doctrine

About the Author

Ezekirel C. Melchisedec is an apostle of Yeshua with a dynamic teaching and preaching anointing to explain the scriptures .He has being a bible teacher since he was a teenager , his books and teachings are spread abroad in the internet .

He is a Ghanaian who has been labouring in outreach ministries , including crusades , online ministry and ministrying in the church Apostle .Ezekiel C. Melchisedec is the founder and the general overseer of the Salvation Christian Church Worldwide ,aka Yeshua Outreach Ministries , a ministry based in Accra, Ghana .

He is married to Pastor Mrs. Favour Melchisedec and together there are working in the vineyard of the Lord .

Milton Keynes UK
Ingram Content Group UK Ltd.
UKHW041814060923
428148UK00001B/29

9 798223 922605

SPEAR OF DESTINY

J.F. PENN

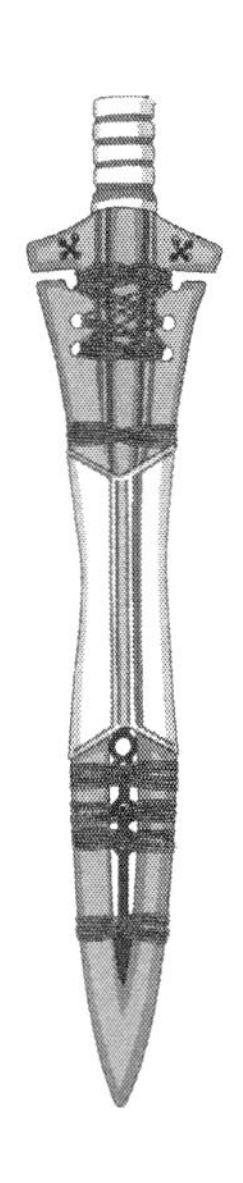

www.JFPenn.com

Special edition hardback ISBN: 978-1-915425-50-8
Hardback ISBN: 978-1-915425-51-5
Paperback ISBN: 978-1-915425-52-2
Large Print ISBN: 978-1-915425-53-9
Ebook ISBN: 978-1-915425-54-6
Audiobook ISBN: 978-1-915425-55-3

Requests to publish work from this book
should be sent to: joanna@JFPenn.com

Cover and interior images generated by J.F. Penn on DALLE and Midjourney with commercial license

Cover and Interior Design: JD Smith Design

www.CurlUpPress.com

"The soldiers put on him a crown of thorns and he was scourged and received condemnation from Pilate, and he was crucified at the place of a skull and two thieves with him, and they gave him vinegar to drink with gall, and Longinus the soldier pierced his side with a spear."

—Gospel of Nicodemus, the Apocrypha

"We may be destroyed, but if we are, we shall drag a world with us—a world in flames."

—Adolf Hitler, quoted in
The Last Days of Hitler by Hugh Trevor-Roper

"I have set before you life and death, blessings and curses... Choose life, so that you and your children may live."

—Deuteronomy 30:19

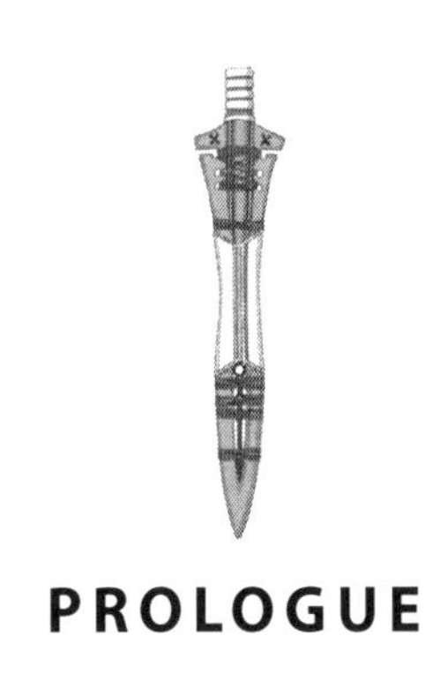

PROLOGUE

DUST MOTES DANCED IN the dim light that filtered through the narrow window high above. Johannes Schell leaned closer to the antique book and squinted at the faded gold leaf title on the cracked spine. Incunabula, books printed before 1500, were his specialty, but this one was a puzzle indeed. He could barely make out the imprinted words and he couldn't pull it down from the shelf until he was clear what he might be working with. It would have to wait until later.

With a frustrated sigh, Johannes pushed his glasses higher on his nose and pulled out the logbook tucked under one arm. He noted the book's approximate location before moving on to the next potential mystery.

The Austrian National Library Archives in Vienna housed over twelve million items in its various collections. How many of them were in this wing — or even in this storeroom — was unknown. Johannes had been assigned by the head librarian to this particular area, which had lain untouched for too long and desperately needed reorganization.

The previous archivist's failing health had resulted in a slackening in documentation and correct storage protocols, and Johannes had inherited disarray and chaos. Decades of unsorted acquisitions overflowed from cabinets around him, spilling haphazardly into every corner, and while sometimes it felt like an overwhelming task, he also sensed a glimmer of excitement at what treasures he might uncover here.

These centuries of books, papers, and curiosities revealed the story of a once-glorious and powerful empire now reduced to a modest republic. There might be personal diaries, obscure philosophical tracts, and hand-drawn maps of vanished borders buried here. Ephemera that might hint at the dark secrets of those who pursued Empire and glory, but inevitably ended up as dust and ashes.

These documents were more than just records of the past. If he could recover long-buried insights, Johannes could ensure these memories lived once more. He might experience, even for just a moment, the long-forgotten thoughts of another person reaching out across the years. The power of words on paper never failed to thrill him, although, of course, most of what he picked through every day were dry books and dull papers, records and receipts that left even the most passionate historian cold.

The hope of discovery was enough to keep him sorting and cataloging, paging through brittle manuscripts and breathing in the dust of generations past. But some days Johannes knew he was losing the battle against entropy's steady creep, as rot and decay devoured humanity's attempts at immortality.

He shifted a teetering pile of leather-bound journals to reach the shelf beyond. As he gingerly tugged out the diary of a little-known seventeenth-century astronomer, the bookcase shifted slightly.

Johannes steadied the heavy oak structure, then peered around it to see what had caused the movement. A small iron latch was just visible against the wood molding and Johannes could make out the dark outline of a door.

He frowned. This door wasn't on any of the maps he knew

of, but the building had been reconfigured multiple times over centuries. As the number of artifacts and manuscripts piled up, old rooms had been filled, their doors closed and not opened again for decades. Perhaps the previous archivist had just piled a load of stuff in there, shut the door, and forgotten about it.

The room probably contained nothing of value: piles of tax records or vehicle requisition forms, the repetitive diaries of unknown Viennese aristocrats.

Or perhaps there might be something far more intriguing.

Johannes looked down at the pile of books he was meant to catalog today. There was no mystery to be solved in those, but the thrill of possibility awaited behind this strange door.

He took a deep breath, shunted the bookcase sideways, and squeezed into the gap to inspect the door more closely.

Dust streaked his jacket, but he barely noticed. His heart pounded as he placed a hand on the wood, considering what might lie behind. He was Howard Carter at the entrance to the tomb of Tutankhamun. He was Flinders Petrie before the Temple of Karnak. After all, the great archaeologists didn't know what they would find until they made their most famous discoveries.

Johannes pushed, then gave the door a shove with his hip.

A faint click sounded within the wall. The narrow door opened a crack, dislodging dust that billowed into the surrounding air.

Coughing a little, Johannes eased the door open just wide enough to squeeze through sideways.

It was pitch dark inside.

He fumbled for a light switch and flicked it on.

As a single bulb buzzed and brightened, Johannes felt the crest of excitement — but his heart sank at what lay within.

The space was the size of a child's bedroom. Perhaps once

a cleaning store cupboard, it was now filled to the ceiling with accounting boxes of moldy cardboard and a few metal filing cabinets that looked many decades old, perhaps from the Second World War period.

It was musty and damp and smelt of decaying paper, old wool, and metal polish. The boxes were stacked so close to the door that Johannes could hardly get into the room. All of this had to be dragged out and examined more carefully. Most likely, these were discarded bureaucratic records that could be shredded and scrapped before the room was used for new archives. Johannes sighed. His curiosity had led to even more hours sorting through even more boring paperwork.

Then he noticed a gap between the stacked boxes.

Johannes peered through, pulling out his trusty pen torch and shining it into the space beyond.

Three suitcases lay piled one atop the other. Next to them, a woman's green beaded handbag, a couple of brass-handled walking sticks, and a child's wooden rocking horse, its paint faded, its mane grey with dust. In one corner stood a dressmaker's dummy swathed in a dress of lace and satin, moth-eaten and spider-webbed.

These must be personal effects, maybe from a wealthy Viennese family caught in the violence of the 1940s and hastily hidden in the hopes of retrieval after the war.

Once again, Johannes considered his options.

Technically, according to the rules, he should retreat and call in help to move the boxes, before investigating officially and documenting everything along the way. But no doubt someone in senior management would take credit for the find, and he would lose access to it completely.

His curiosity drove him on. There might be something far more interesting in the suitcases. He would report it, of course, but he wouldn't know what to report unless he investigated further.

Johannes slowly shifted a tower of bulging document boxes to make a narrow path between them. He edged his way into the back section of the room, folding himself through the restricted space until he reached the personal effects.

He ran his fingertips over the top suitcase and tried the latches.

They clicked open, and he pulled up the lid.

Johannes gasped at the sight of a crisp red Nazi flag folded within, the swastika clearly visible. He lifted the edge. An iron cross medal lay on top of a stack of papers and photographs bearing the eagle insignia of the Third Reich.

Remnants of Europe's most devastating war were not uncommon in Vienna. Most were in official archives, protected from being sold to those who idolized the Führer, those who still wanted the change he sought to deliver at the expense of the lives of millions. In these modern times, Europe was once again on the brink of a wider war, spreading out from conflict in the East. With a refugee crisis and ongoing economic struggles, some chanted the same slogans and urged the same actions as the Nazis, even if their words were thinly veiled with nationalist rhetoric.

As a historian, Johannes was devoted to preserving his country's past, even when it repulsed him. But he didn't have to enjoy doing it.

He closed the lid and lifted the suitcase from the pile, then opened the one beneath. Inside was an old machine nestled among yellowed maps and spiral notebooks, its black casing dulled by time.

Johannes recognized it instantly as a device used to encode wartime messages. The Allies had broken its cipher, although the Nazis didn't realize the fact until it was too late.

It was an Enigma machine.

He'd never seen one in person and the device was smaller than he expected, less substantial than its historic weight.

The series of rotors on top, each marked with letters of the alphabet, were now frozen in place. The adjacent keys were yellowed with age, the letters on them faded but still discernible. Johannes could almost hear the clacking of those keys in a dark, smoke-filled room, encoding messages that directed movements of troops and U-boats, carrying orders that would change the course of the war.

The Enigma machines had facilitated Nazi conquest in the early years of the war, their impenetrable cipher crucial to Blitzkrieg dominance. The efficient encryption also shrouded SS directives for deportations and mass murder in concentration camps, as the engines of genocide fired up in the Final Solution.

British and Polish code breakers finally cracked the secret messages after years of failure, and once Germany lost their advantage, the tide turned, and the Allies began to take back ground.

Johannes reached out and carefully gripped both sides of the machine. He lifted it out and tilted it to check underneath for a maker's mark or inspection stamp.

Faint engraving marked the box as from the Berlin factory of Heimsoeth & Rinke. A valuable unit indeed, most likely used by intelligence or high command.

A rustle came from within as he moved the machine.

Johannes tilted it once more. There was definitely something inside.

He placed the machine down and inspected the wooden sides and base. As he ran his fingers over the smartly dovetailed joins, he sensed subtle irregular bumps on the bottom.

He pressed along the seam. A faint click came from within as a slim panel shifted. A shallow, hidden drawer popped out with a folded and yellowed piece of paper nestled inside.

Heart thudding and hardly daring to breathe, Johannes gently unfolded the corners of the paper.

The handwritten German note was hard to make out,

and what he could discern made little sense as it was in code. But the drawing on one side made Johannes's heart beat even faster. It depicted a Roman spearhead beside a stark SS lightning rune.

He knew that spear. It lay in the Schatzkammer, the treasury of the Hofburg Museum, within walking distance of the library he stood in right now.

It was the Heilige Lanze, the Holy Lance.

The Spear of Destiny.

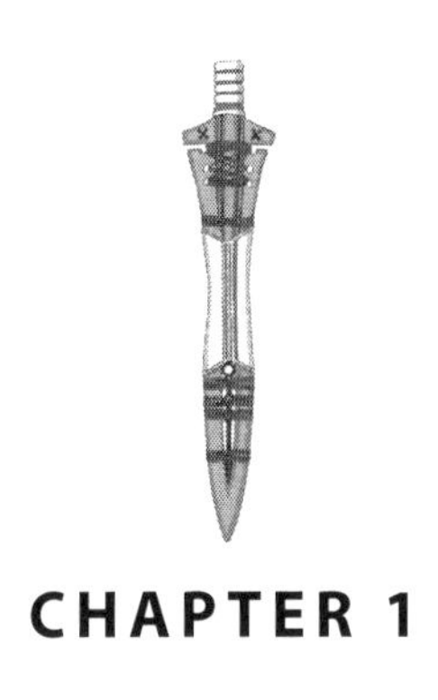

CHAPTER 1

THE CHILL OF WINTER hung heavy in the air as Morgan Sierra pushed open the ancient wrought-iron gates of Wolvercote Cemetery on the outskirts of Oxford, England. Skeletal branches of leafless trees loomed over the gravestones as she walked slowly along the winding path. Her boots crunched softly on the thin layer of frost that clung to the carpet of dead leaves as the harsh caw of a crow broke the silence.

The cemetery in its winter shroud was bleak, but in the sheltered root system of an old oak, Morgan spotted the fresh green shoots of early snowdrops. She couldn't help but smile at nature's optimism.

The seasons would turn again, and 'this too shall pass,' as Ben used to say, quoting the old Persian adage that summed up the ephemeral nature of life. Ben had never been afraid of death, even though it had come for him violently in the end, and while Morgan thought of him often, she needed him now more than ever.

She finally reached the corner of the cemetery reserved for monks and friars. Father Ben Costanza's simple headstone was unassuming but dignified, as befitted a Dominican monk who spent his life in service to God and his students at Blackfriars College.

Ben had been a close friend of her mother's and had promised to protect the family after her death. But he had been far more to Morgan than a teacher and mentor.

She sighed, her breath misting in the air. As she stood amongst the tombstones, it seemed that death crept ever closer. Her parents were long gone — her mother from cancer, her father from a terrorist bomb. Her husband, Elian, had been killed in a hail of bullets on the Golan Heights when they served together in the Israel Defense Force. And Father Ben, whose death came in the wake of an ARKANE mission he should not even have been involved in.

The Arcane Religious Knowledge And Numinous Experience (ARKANE) Institute specialized in solving religious and supernatural mysteries around the world, and Morgan had joined them a few years back as an agent. She had thought the work would answer some of her deeper questions, but her curiosity about what lay beyond the veil of the visible world only multiplied with each mission.

She curled her fingers around a small, smooth pebble in her pocket, then placed it gently on top of Father Ben's grave next to all the others. Each stone already there was a symbol of her many visits, her unspoken conversations, her respect for the man she missed so much.

She reached out to trace the engraved letters on the headstone and whispered a prayer to the god Ben believed in. The harrowing events of the ARKANE missions had never shaken his faith, and Morgan wished he was here now. She needed his advice, because she felt lost in a darkness that sank deeper into her bones every day.

A sudden gust of wind whipped around the cemetery. She pulled her coat tighter around her as the memory resurfaced.

She was back in the dimly lit chamber of the Northumbrian citadel, the air thick with the stench of decay and ancient dust. Morgan struggled to escape the bonds of shadow that held her to the altar as the Black Anchorite loomed above her.

His skin was a mosaic of grafted dead flesh, writhing under the flickering torchlight. His breath wheezed, each inhalation a theft of life, each exhalation a death rattle, as he offered her an unholy gift of immortality.

He wrenched the tainted miracle of a heart from his chest. The blackened, pulsating organ dripped with blood as its dark veins curled toward her.

Morgan's heart pounded, her palms sweating, as she remembered those final moments — the pull of the heart's corrupt power, the visceral smell of blood and incense — before she found the strength to throw the cursed organ into the flames.

But the words of the Black Anchorite still echoed in her mind, words spoken as his cursed flesh collapsed into dust and fragments of bone.

"For what you have destroyed, you will suffer a blood torment that time can never heal..."

As his rasping breath faded, Morgan shivered in the chill of the cemetery.

Her partner agent at ARKANE, Jake Timber, had been there in the moments after and dismissed the curse as an empty threat. But he did not experience the power of the heart or glimpse the true dark nature of the Black Anchorite.

The curse was real. Morgan was sure of it.

In recent days, she had submitted to a battery of tests in the ARKANE medical labs, but they found nothing. No markers in her blood, no new mutations, even though drops of tainted ichor had burned her skin.

Father Ben had always given her a fresh perspective, weaving his deep religious faith with an encyclopedic knowledge of the occult and supernatural.

"What should I do, Ben?" Morgan whispered.

She closed her eyes and imagined standing in his old

study at Blackfriars, drinking his special blend of chai. In answer to any question, he would pull down a book from his extensive collection and quote some long dead theologian or philosopher.

Morgan sighed, her breath a cloud of vapor in the frigid air.

If she was honest with herself, she knew what Ben would say. 'Take another step forward, and trust that you will figure it out along the way.' While Ben had his doubts about some within ARKANE, he had never doubted Morgan.

He had also left his extensive collection of books to the ARKANE library, which lay within the Institute's labyrinthine complex under the Museum of Natural History in the centre of Oxford. Perhaps she might find some answers there, and it was at least a practical next step.

Morgan took one last look at Ben's grave, then turned away, her footsteps quicker now as she traced the path back to the lych-gate.

As she reached the boundary of the cemetery, the threshold between the dead and the living, her phone rang.

The shrill tone pierced the atmosphere of silent reverence, and she walked quickly outside the gate toward the road beyond. She fumbled in her pocket, her fingers numb from the cold, and pulled it out.

She took a deep breath and answered. "Hey, Jake. I'm just on my way back."

"You're still in Oxford?"

Morgan could hear his concern. They had been through so much together and even though there was much unspoken between them, their bond was close.

"Yes, I'm still here. I'm going to search through Ben's old books and see what I can find about blood curses."

"That's going to have to wait. I need you with me in Vienna."

Morgan turned to look back at the cemetery, imagining

the peace of the dead beneath the earth. How easy it would be to join them.

"Can someone else handle this with you? I need more time to figure out this curse."

"The Black Anchorite is dead, Morgan. The heart was burned. But the world doesn't stop." Jake's voice softened. "I know you. You're stronger than any curse, and we've faced down worse together. This is what we do. Besides, I know you're going to want to be part of this."

His words piqued Morgan's curiosity. "Why? What do you have?"

"An old letter hidden in a long lost Nazi Enigma machine. A letter about the Holy Lance, the Spear of Destiny. Come to Vienna and you can see it for yourself. It's only a few hours' flight. You can be here by early evening."

Morgan hesitated a moment, but the familiar quickening at a new mission outpaced her fear. It would be another step forward, at least.

"I'm on my way."

As Morgan hurried down the road, her stride grew more confident, more purposeful. Each step away from the grave was a step back into the world of the living, a world of supernatural mystery, of ancient relics and obscure secrets.

She would join Jake in Vienna, and perhaps he was right. Perhaps the curse was nothing at all.

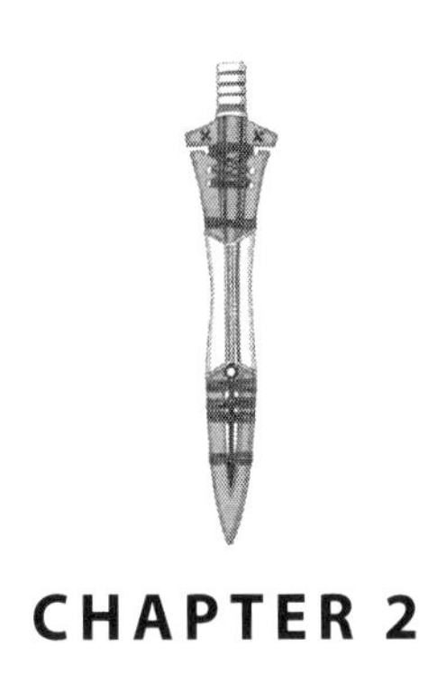

CHAPTER 2

LATER THAT EVENING, MORGAN stepped out of a taxi by the Schatzkammer, the Imperial Treasury of Vienna. It was even colder here in the capital of Austria, and Morgan tightened her coat as she looked around the deserted square.

The regal Hofburg Palace complex resonated with the echoes of a bygone era. Statues of gods and lions stood as silent sentinels, once representing the power of the Austro-Hungarian Habsburg dynasty and now consigned to history. The wind carried whispers of centuries past, of power and intrigue that once pulsed through the heart of an empire that commanded most of Europe. Now its glory was gone, its majesty faded like ink in the dusty records of history.

The treasury loomed ahead, its entrance a grand gateway emblazoned with intricate gold and russet designs along with a regal coat of arms. A single streetlamp lit a path to the gateway.

Jake Timber stepped out of the shadows, a thick coat covering his muscular frame. Morgan walked over to meet him, a smile on her lips.

Jake was her partner agent at ARKANE, but he had also become far more than that over their many missions together. They had saved each other's lives countless times, and their shared history gave them a bond that strayed into feelings neither would speak aloud. They had both lost so many loved ones that neither of them was ready to tempt fate again.

"Glad you could make it." Jake grinned, and the faint corkscrew scar above his left eyebrow twisted a little. "I know the mystery of the Spear will take your mind off that curse."

"I'm certainly intrigued. Legend says the Spear belonged to Longinus, the Roman centurion who pierced the side of Christ on the cross. But there are many other relics that claim to be the real spear, so why are we interested in this one?"

As they walked through the gateway into the square beyond, Jake pulled out his phone and tapped through to an image of a yellowed page.

"This was found inside a previously undiscovered Enigma machine, decoded easily with modern decryption software. It's a letter from an SS officer to Heinrich Himmler, but I want you to see the relic first and make your own judgment before I tell you what it says."

The SS lightning runes on the letter sent a shiver down Morgan's spine. Despite the decades since the Nazis had been thwarted in their attempt to kill every Jew in Europe, those who still upheld the principles of the Third Reich cast a long shadow once more. There were many who said the conditions in Europe now mirrored those in the 1930s, when Hitler's party cast a destructive spell over the most cultured of nations.

As agents of ARKANE, she and Jake followed threads of religion and violence woven across centuries into modern day mystery. Blades still pierced the flesh of the living, just as the lance had pierced the side of Christ, and some wounds never heal completely.

Jake led them to a nondescript entrance in the corner of the square. Two stony-faced security guards in immaculate uniforms stood by the door, next to a far more enthusiastic young man. He was tall and slender with a lopsided grin, and wore a brown corduroy jacket flecked with dust. As they approached, he thrust out his hand to shake theirs.

"I'm Johannes. I found the letter that brings you here on this mysterious quest, and I shall be your guide to the Spear of Destiny."

His eyes lit up with excitement as he spoke and his hands trembled slightly as he pointed the way inside.

Morgan and Jake followed Johannes inside the halls of the treasury. The rooms were dimly lit to preserve the colors of the regal and sacred artifacts within. Glass cases shimmered in the muted light. They were almost works of art themselves — constructed of carved and gilded wood, lined with faded velvet — as if each one cradled not mere physical objects but time itself, encapsulated in gold and gemstones.

Portraits of solemn-faced monarchs peered down from the walls, their names wielding great power within their lifetimes but now forgotten, as all must one day be.

Johannes walked on past cases filled with the regalia of power: crowns that had graced the heads of emperors, scepters that once directed the fate of nations. He pointed up at a picture of a corpulent king in splendid robes.

"The Habsburgs were not just rulers; they were the architects of hundreds of years of European history. They orchestrated political marriages that linked kingdoms, and their strategic alliances and conflicts set the stage for the modern political and cultural landscape. The peace treaties, the shifting of power, the art and architecture you see across Europe — all lead back, in some way, to the Habsburgs." He sighed and shook his head. "Vienna was once a great power, perhaps even the center of the world. It's hard to believe that now."

He led them on to rooms filled with reliquaries, each precious for their gold and jewels, but more spiritually treasured for the fragments of bone and blood — the relics of saints — that lay within.

Morgan noticed a Baroque reliquary bust of St Matthew, rays of gold encircling his head in a halo, his face contorted in a silent scream of martyrdom.

A fourteenth-century reliquary originally from Prague lay in a nearby case, its gilded peak reaching toward heaven. The central glass cylinder held a single tooth encased within filigree of gold, hanging suspended on a thread.

Morgan frowned at the unusual object and bent to read the label: The tooth of John the Baptist. That was… interesting.

She still found the Catholic obsession with bodily relics strange, even after so many ARKANE missions centering on them. Raised in Israel by her Jewish father, separate from her Catholic mother, her own tradition focused on the unseen and the spiritual, an intangible god without form or physicality.

Perhaps the relics were part of a human need to see and touch objects of belief, to make tangible the divine stories that shaped faith. Like Thomas placing his fingers into the bleeding side of the resurrected Christ, these objects gave the faithful an anchor.

But the question remained: how many were body parts of random dead people sold by a corrupt church, and how many were real relics with a power that could touch the physical realm?

Morgan would have once said that all relics were fake, a way for the church to control the masses. But after what she had seen on her ARKANE missions — in the temple at Abu Simbel in Egypt, at the Western Wall in Jerusalem, and in the heart of the citadel — it was clear that some relics held great power. It was just hard to find them in a labyrinth of counterfeits. Which would this Spear of Destiny be?

Johannes spun around as he led them into another room,

its walls a dark burgundy hung with more portraits of dead royalty.

He waved his arms with a flourish. "Behold the imperial regalia."

The Imperial Crown rested in the middle of the room in its own case, raised up on a dais and spot-lit so its jewels reflected facets of light. It was a kaleidoscope of color, almost gaudy with bright stones and gleaming gold. The Imperial Orb lay in a nearby case, alongside scepters and the Imperial Sword of St Mauritius.

These symbols of power and dominion over millions of people and lands stretching across Europe now sat largely ignored in their display cases. Evidence that temporal power is transient and even the greatest empires must fall, even if those who rule them believe they never will.

Johannes pointed at a case in the corner of the room. "Here are the most important religious relics of empire, including the Heilige Lanze, the Holy Lance, known as the Spear of Destiny."

The display case was dominated by a huge gold cross encrusted with jewels, an eleventh-century vessel made to hold the precious relics. On its left lay the Heilige Lanze, and on the right, the Particle of the True Cross, a piece of wood encased in precious metal.

The Spear was smaller than Morgan expected, but then it was merely the point, without the long shaft needed to wield the weapon. It was a fusion of steel and iron, strong enough to bear the weight of its own legend. Its metal was aged to a dull sheen and it was bound with wire in a decorative pattern, with a band of silver and gold covering its midsection. Strands of wire anchored a nail, said to be from the hand of Christ crucified, into its tip.

Morgan bent to examine the Spear more closely through the glass.

She imagined its blade forced deep into a dying man's side

before being wrenched free as blood poured out. Whether or not that man had been Jesus, this spear had certainly caused the death of many. History was written with blades of iron and ink of blood, and this spear, real or not, cast a long shadow.

That shadow reached Morgan now, creating a chill deep inside.

She took a deep breath and stood tall again, shaking her head to dispel the darker thoughts that twisted around her. The threat of the curse sent her mind into desolate places and she needed to get back to her usual practical self.

Johannes recounted the legend of the artifact, his voice tinged with reverence.

"Some say that when the Roman centurion Longinus pierced the side of Christ, his spear was already a talisman of power. It could have been the spear of Herod Antipas, King of the Jews, passed down through generations from the hand of Joshua, who breached the walls of Jericho. Even before then, it might have been the spear hurled at a young David from the hand of King Saul, before David rose to become the most powerful—"

"What about modern times?" Jake interrupted.

Johannes took a breath before continuing. "Of course. Many rulers and warriors held the Spear, channeling its earthly and spiritual power to win great battles. The Roman emperor Constantine, the Holy Roman Emperor Charlemagne, and, of course, the Habsburgs. When not borne into battle, the Lance lay here at the Hofburg until 1938."

Morgan nodded. "The Anschluss, of course."

Johannes explained further. "Indeed. When Hitler annexed Austria in 1938, it became part of the German Reich. He took possession of the imperial regalia, as well as the Heilige Lanze, and ordered it all taken to Nuremberg."

"Why did Hitler want the Lance in particular?" Jake asked.

Johannes frowned and shuffled his feet, clearly uncomfortable with this aspect of his country's history. "When Hitler was a poor art student here in Vienna, he visited the Spear many times. He stood here for hours contemplating it, and records show he researched its history in the state library, as well as aspects of the occult. Legend tells that whoever possesses the Spear holds destiny on the tip of its blade, and whoever holds it in battle will never be defeated — but only if they offer a blood sacrifice. The greater the sacrifice, the stronger the power. As the far right rises again across the nations of Europe, there are rumors of those who seek the Spear once more."

In the silence that followed, Morgan considered the enormity of Hitler's blood sacrifice. Six million Jews – as well as Roma and other ethnic groups, political prisoners, homosexuals and those considered deviant – were murdered in the death camps, on top of the war waged across continents. There were around eighty million dead across Europe by the end of the most deadly war the world had ever seen.

Jake broke the silence. "But Hitler lost the war."

Johannes nodded. "Yes, he killed himself in the bunker in Berlin on 30 April 1945, but it turned out that the Allies took possession of the Spear in Nuremberg on 20 April, ten days before. Hitler lost the Spear before he lost the war and his life."

As his words echoed in the darkened room, it seemed to Morgan that the stink of smoke and charred flesh suddenly rose around them, and flames crackled as bodies burned in the ultimate sacrifice.

Hitler's belief in the spear, whether it was real or not, gave it power even generations after his death. There would always be those who sought to control destiny, and darkness was rising once more.

A cacophony of gunfire suddenly shattered the hush of the treasury.

Returning fire rang out, silenced quickly.

Johannes stood frozen, his eyes wide with terror.

Morgan spun to Jake. Neither had thought this place a threat. Neither of them were armed.

"We have to get out of here." The gunfire, muffled slightly by how deep they were inside the building, sounded as if it had come from the direction of the entrance. Morgan gestured to the Lance. "But what if they're here for this?"

Running footsteps sounded from the outer rooms of the treasury. A small team, clearly not expecting much resistance.

They were only a few rooms away — and getting closer.

Jake seized a fire extinguisher from the side of the room, hefting it high — and slammed it down on the display case.

The glass shattered. An alarm cut through a renewed barrage of gunfire, its shrill note high and piercing.

Morgan reached in and grabbed the Lance, as Jake pulled Johannes away.

They raced together into the next room — as a hail of gunfire tore into the imperial regalia right behind them.

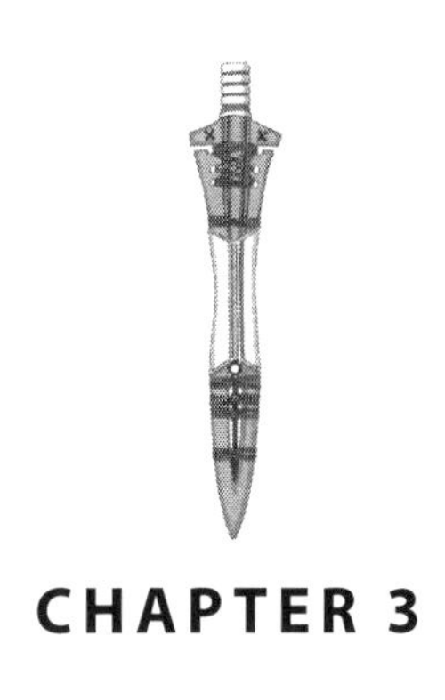

CHAPTER 3

"WHICH WAY?" JAKE SHOOK Johannes as he half-ran, half-dragged the archivist along.

They darted between the display cases, Morgan following behind as the gunfire fell silent. She imagined the assailants entering the room of priceless treasures. Had they come for the imperial regalia?

Her hopes were dashed almost immediately.

"They must have the Spear. Go! Go!" The man's voice was deep, resonant with military authority — and his accent was American.

That gave Morgan pause. Why was an American military team after the relic?

"This way." Johannes ducked through a service door. Beyond it, a concrete staircase led in two opposite directions.

He headed quickly downstairs and Jake followed, but Morgan hesitated. Whoever it was, they wanted the Spear, and without weapons, their best chance was to split up. She did not want Johannes's blood on her hands.

"Get him to safety," she urged Jake, and sprinted up the stairs away from them, the Spear in her hand.

She heard a muttered curse from Jake as she raced upwards. He would want to fight alongside her, but they also trusted each other's skills. He would get Johannes to safety, and perhaps she might discover more about those who sought the Spear.

As Morgan sprinted up the stairs, she heard the door open on the landing below — then footsteps running both up and down as the attack team split up.

Her breath was ragged as she reached the top of the staircase and burst out of the fire escape onto the roof of the Hofburg Treasury.

The State Hall's majestic dome loomed ahead, and before her, a vast expanse of centuries-old stone tiles worn smooth by the passage of time. Ornate stone chimneys and intricately carved decorative elements cast deep shadows across the rooftop. They offered shelter, but not enough.

A narrow metal walkway clung precariously to the side of the roof, hanging suspended between the steeply sloping tiles and a dizzying four-story drop to the hard stone square below.

There was no other route. She had to go on.

Morgan ran, her footsteps thudding along the metal in a cacophony that her pursuers would have no trouble following. She had to get off this roof.

She scanned the area as she raced on, heart pounding, legs tiring, as she gripped the Spear in one hand. While Morgan had been skeptical back in the treasury, the attention of this group made her more determined to protect the relic, whatever it might be.

A bullet whistled past her ear — so close that she could feel the displaced vibration.

A shout from the rooftop behind.

Morgan ducked. Her foot skidded on the frost-slicked metal.

She caught herself with her free hand on the sloping tiles, hunkering behind a row of marble statues as a hail of gunfire pinged against the roof.

She risked a look back.

There were only two of them, but they were close.

Looking around for another route, she spotted a tiny window higher up. It was wedged open and, with some luck, it would take her pursuers time to figure out where she went.

She crouched low behind the marble statues, and quietly clambered up the tiles, climbing through the window into a storeroom.

As the men drew closer below her, Morgan ducked low beneath the sill, trying to control her breathing.

Footsteps grew louder below.

She braced herself, ready to run, but they walked directly below the window, hurrying on, presuming she had continued along the walkway out of sight. But they were clearly professionals, and it wouldn't be long until they circled back.

Morgan darted out of the storeroom and ran down a narrow wooden flight of stairs. They widened onto a landing at the bottom, and then opened out further into a grand marble hallway, with towering pillars and stairs leading further down.

This must be the adjoining building, the Österreichische Nationalbibliothek, the National Library and State Hall. There was no time to stop and admire its beauty as Morgan sprinted down, the Spear gripped tightly in her hand. If she couldn't find another weapon, or a place of safety, she needed somewhere to hide.

She darted through a gap between a pair of gigantic double doors and found herself in the State Hall.

It was a literary cathedral, a temple to knowledge, with shelves of leather-bound books stretching up to the high ceiling. Domes of brightly colored frescoes depicted figures of terrestrial beauty alongside violent war and conquest. They echoed the dual nature of humanity, capable of both creation and destruction, in homage to the grandeur of the Austro-Hungarian empire.

Four gigantic Venetian globes stood in the corners of

the vast hall, their painted lines evidence of a time when the world was still a mystery, when cartographers still charted unknown waters.

While the surface of the world might now be mapped, there were still mysteries, and as she ran on down the marble hallway, Morgan wondered what forgotten knowledge lay in these ancient tomes. Perhaps there was an answer here — to the truth of the Spear, or a clue to her curse. If only she had time to linger.

A bang came from upstairs, the window of the attic slamming against its casing.

She didn't have long.

Morgan weaved through the hall, staying close to the towering bookcases. As the footsteps grew louder, she ducked into a shadowed niche and sheltered behind one of the massive Venetian globes next to a high ladder. She calmed her breathing as she pressed her back against the wall of books.

The double doors creaked open.

The hollow sound of footsteps echoed through the grand hall, magnified by the cavernous space. It was only one person, the tread heavy enough to be a man. The team must have split up in order to search more of the enormous library complex.

Morgan shifted her grip on the Spear, turning the relic into a weapon, readying herself.

She exhaled slowly, allowing her years of Krav Maga martial arts and combat training with the Israeli Defense Force to surface. She didn't seek conflict, but the warrior in her was always ready to fight. The shadow of death was a constant companion for her people, and in her land. She would not seek its embrace, but neither would she shy away from it when it came calling.

From her concealed position, Morgan watched the solitary figure advance down the marble corridor, his movements deliberate and practiced.

The man moved quickly with the quiet confidence of a predator, his gun held outstretched before him. He wore black military gear, with no insignia that might betray his allegiance.

His face was etched with scars and stubble, his jaw set in a hard, determined line — the visage of a man who had known many battles and carried their legacy on his skin.

Morgan sensed a lethal calm in him. He had faced down death and walked away unflinching from those he had left behind. She had to disarm him, then at least she might have a chance. As the man advanced, she tightened her grip on the Spear, letting its weight become an extension of her arm.

The moment his foot crossed the threshold where shadow met light, Morgan struck.

She darted out, low and lethal.

He spun around, his gun coming up in a professional reflex — but she was a wraith, a shadow in motion. She closed the gap and swept her arm up and out in a practiced arc, an inside deflection that redirected the muzzle of the gun.

Bullets raked the shelves as he fired.

Morgan jabbed an elbow strike to his head. As he reared back, she used the end of the Spear to thrust into a pressure point on his arm.

He dropped the gun, stumbled back, his surprise evident at her ferocity. Morgan kicked his gun away as they circled each other.

"I just want the Spear," he said, gaze fixed on her. "I don't know who you are and I don't care. Just drop it and go."

He reached forward to grab her, arm outstretched.

Anticipating his move, Morgan side-stepped and delivered a hammer fist strike to his ear.

He spun from the blow and staggered into the Venetian globe with a crash. It rocked precariously, tipping him off balance. He dropped to his hands and knees, shaking his head to clear his vision.

Morgan turned to sprint away.

He lunged after her with a roar, managing to grab a handful of her hair. He spun her to the ground. Morgan gasped as she smashed into the cold marble. The Spear fell from her hand and clattered to the ground.

He charged after it.

Morgan rolled to her feet in a practiced movement and barreled into him, knocking him away from the relic.

He followed her down, pinning her to the floor, one arm beneath her, his heavily muscled body on top of her torso. He was incredibly strong, almost unnaturally so.

Morgan hip thrust and rolled, trying to throw him off.

She managed to get one hand free — gouged at his eyes — but he grabbed her hand, twisting it back over her head. With his other hand, he gripped her throat and began to choke her.

Pinned down, the cold press of the floor at her back, Morgan's world narrowed. She saw the pores of his skin, the lines of a rune tattoo on his neck, the healed scars on his face. The promise of his grip was oblivion, and part of her welcomed its embrace.

But as his fingertips touched the pulse in her neck, he hesitated.

Their gaze locked and Morgan felt a jolt of connection. This man was far more than he seemed.

His eyes widened. He loosened his grip on her neck, his grasp faltering. His breath was a ghost across her skin as he whispered, "Who are you to be so cursed?"

Morgan lay immobile for a beat as the chill of his words pierced her. He clambered off, grabbing the Spear from the floor and his gun from where it lay.

She rose to her feet as he raced away down the hall.

"Who are you?" she called after him. "How do you know?"

He turned at the end of the hallway in front of the double

doors. Their gazes locked once more, then he darted out, the prize of the Spear in his hand.

* * *

As Gabriel Blackthorn sprinted down the marble staircase away from the State Hall, he pressed the comms button on his radio.

"Package acquired. Meet back at alpha base."

His team would scatter and rendezvous later, and the precision of a mission planned and executed satisfied him, but his mind still reeled at the encounter in the library.

The woman — the fighter — haunted him.

She was clearly military of some kind but she wasn't armed for a mission or dressed for combat. With her dark curls and lightly muscled frame, she could have been a curator at the museum, but her unusual cobalt blue eyes, the right bisected with a slash of violet, had seemed to gaze right into his soul.

But it wasn't her striking looks he couldn't get out of his mind. It was the electric sensation he felt when his hand touched her neck, when he felt her pulse against his bare skin.

Her blood was like his. Tainted somehow.

Who was she? What was she?

As Gabriel hurried out into the street and jogged away from the Hofburg complex, he resolved to find out who the woman was and why she sought the Spear of Destiny. But in the meantime, he needed to report back.

Once he was several streets away, Gabriel pulled out his phone and sent an encrypted text. *Mission accomplished.*

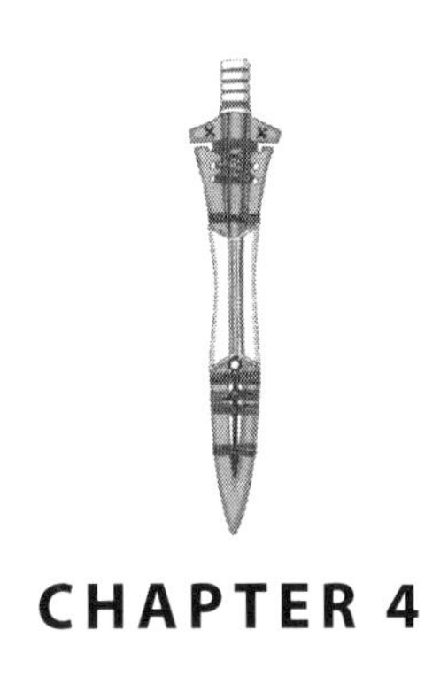

CHAPTER 4

THE CHANTS ECHOED THROUGH the stone walls of the Capitol in the heart of Washington, DC, muffled but unmistakable.

"Strong-hold! Strong-hold! Strong-hold!"

General Ezekiel Stronghold stood unmoving in the shadows, listening, feeling the energy build. The syllables of his name pulsed like a heartbeat, like the marching feet of soldiers in formation going to war.

His hand went unconsciously to his chest, fingers tracing the outline of the silver ring that hung beneath his military uniform, a reminder of the great work begun so long ago.

"Hold strong," his grandfather rasped on his deathbed, pressing the SS death's head ring into young Ezekiel's palm. The old man's eyes gleamed with fervor as he spoke of the plan. The seeds planted two generations ago, and the glorious harvest to come.

From Berlin to Langley, Nuremberg to Washington, DC, his family had nurtured the vision, positioning themselves in the new world, ready for a singular moment when the greatest nation on earth would be ready for a strong leader to emerge.

Now in his early sixties, with decades of military experience and honors behind him, it was Ezekiel's destiny to light the fire that would cleanse the country of festering rot and usher in a new era.

As he put his palm over the hidden ring, sensing the weight of providence in his bones, his phone vibrated in his pocket.

He glanced at the screen: *Mission accomplished.*

Gabriel had succeeded, and the first fragment of the Spear was almost in Ezekiel's grasp. Truly a sign that his bid for the presidency was righteous indeed. The Spear of Longinus, the blade that pierced the side of Christ, would be the key to unlocking a new epoch, built on the ashes of those who stood against it.

The chanting grew louder — a thunder of voices, the beat of a war drum.

It was time.

Ezekiel ascended the stairs. At the top, out of sight of the crowd, he paused and allowed the weight of history to settle on his shoulders like a sacred mantle. He exhaled slowly, centering himself.

Ezekiel stepped out, emerging into the blinding sun before a sea of upturned faces and waving flags.

The roar of the crowd crashed over him like a wave and for a minute, he let his spirit soar on its energy.

He raised his hands, and a hush fell over the masses. They gazed up at him and Ezekiel sensed their yearning for a mighty leader to take them into a new age where they could be proud of their country again. Where the USA was once more the strongest, the most respected — the most feared — nation on earth.

In that charged silence, he sensed the certainty of his calling. He was the tip of the spear that would pierce the heart of a fallen nation. Let the blood of renewal flow. Let the great work begin.

"We gather today in the presence of Almighty God, in the shadow of this great Capitol, to affirm our sacred destiny.

This nation was chosen to be a light unto the world, a city on a hill. We are the chosen people, called to lead the nations to righteousness. But our divine calling is under siege."

Ezekiel's voice deepened, his expression severe. "The forces of darkness have infiltrated our institutions, poisoned the minds of our children, turned the sacred idea of family upside down, and corrupted the very soul of our nation. They come in many guises, like wolves in sheep's clothing, but their agenda is the same: to tear down everything our forefathers built, to replace our God-given values with twisted moral relativism."

The crowd roared their discontent, lifting their banners high, faces contorted with righteous anger.

Ezekiel leaned onto the podium, his eyes blazing as he gazed out over the crowd.

"This country has strayed far from the path of righteousness. Prayer has been banished from our schools, the unborn are slaughtered in the womb, and the sacred bond of marriage has been defiled. Our once-proud cities have become cesspools of crime and degeneracy, overrun by illegal immigrants and welfare parasites. The America we knew, the nation of our fathers, is slipping away."

The crowd responded with a chorus of boos and jeers, a howl of despair and fury. Ezekiel let it sink into him, absorbing their anger and their pain. He would be the voice of the forgotten, the forsaken, and together they would rise.

"But I tell you this," he thundered, his voice rising above the din. "If we do not take a stand now, if we do not fight for what we know is true, we will face a terrible future. The Book of Revelation speaks of a time of great tribulation, a time when nation shall rise against nation, and the Antichrist will rule over a fallen world."

Ezekiel paused, letting the specter of apocalypse hang in the air. He fed on the crowd's fear, their desperate hunger for hope. He softened his tone.

"But the Bible speaks also of a remnant, a faithful few who hold fast to the truth, who will be a light in the darkness. I believe that remnant is here today, on the steps of this Capitol, and in every home that believes we can be a great nation once more. If we can only hold strong to our mission."

Murmurs of assent rippled through the crowd — heads nodding, eyes shining with newfound purpose.

Ezekiel gripped the podium, his knuckles white. "We have allowed the godless to chip away at our foundation, stone by stone. We have allowed our blood to be poisoned. But it is not too late. We can still reclaim our heritage and restore our nation to its former glory. However, we must be willing to fight. It will be painful, but we must cut out the rot and burn it before it destroys us all."

The crowd erupted in cheers and applause, a tidal wave of sound that crashed against the Capitol steps. Ezekiel basked in it, feeling the energy flow through him.

Suddenly, a commotion broke out at the back of the throng. Angry voices rose above the din with cries of "Fascist!", "Bigot!", "Racist!"

A group of protesters pushed their way forward, waving signs and chanting slogans.

A phalanx of black-clad security guards rallied around them, members of Jericho Command, Ezekiel's personal militia. They moved with ruthless efficiency, wrestling the protesters to the ground and roughly dragging them away. This was no gentle persuasion, but swift, brutal action, a display of force.

The crowd stirred, unsettled by the sudden violence.

Ezekiel raised a hand. A hush fell over the plaza.

"Forces will rise against us. Enemies of faith. Servants of chaos. They will try to silence us, intimidate us, turn us away from our righteous path."

The crowd murmured its assent, a low rumble of anger.

Ezekiel's tone turned gentle. "We must pray for them." He bowed his head. "Pray for the lost, the misguided, those who have succumbed to the siren call of the easy path."

Thousands of heads lowered, a wave of reverence washing over the plaza. Ezekiel waited a moment, then continued, his tone hard once more.

"We will pray for them, but we will not be stopped. We will stand firm in our faith, in our mission, no matter the cost. War may come, and we will fight it. The battle is ours to win."

The crowd erupted in cheers, a deafening roar of affirmation. They were one body now, one heart, one purpose. And at their head, Ezekiel stood tall and unshakeable.

He raised his hands for quiet once more, his voice booming out. "Will you stand with me? Will you help me take back this nation for God and country?"

The roar of assent was deafening, and in that moment, Ezekiel knew the mantle of destiny indeed lay upon him. Once the completed Spear was in his hand, nothing could stop the reckoning to come.

The chant rose louder than before, a thunderous mantra. "Strong-hold! Strong-hold! Strong-hold!"

Ezekiel stood basking in the adulation. Then, with a final wave, he turned and strode offstage, back inside the hallways of the Capitol.

His aides crowded around, while behind them, senators and senior figures from both political parties waited to speak with him. No doubt they wished to pledge their support and endorse his candidacy after seeing the success of the event. His campaign would be unstoppable now, and they would all want a piece of it.

But they could wait.

Ezekiel raised his hand and half-bowed his head, a gesture of well-practiced humility. "Thank you all for your support. I need fifteen minutes alone to pray, but then I will meet with each of you." He looked pointedly at the most prominent political figures present. "Together, we will set this country on a new path."

He gestured to one of his aides, who he trusted to organize the many meetings that would stem from his triumphant speech.

Others in his team would already be publishing video clips, amplifying viral social media memes, and running new ads. His message would spread swiftly across the nation and the world. The people wanted a strong leader — and now they had one.

Ezekiel strode along the corridor to his private office and closed the door, locking it to make sure he would not be disturbed.

He exhaled slowly, welcoming the reprieve. His whole body thrummed with energy, his heart beating fast after the adulation of the crowd. It was a heady drug, indeed.

Ezekiel poured himself a glass of water and drank it down, just one aspect of his spartan health regime. His body was a temple, after all, and physical fitness and peak health were a prerequisite for a vigorous leader.

In keeping with this philosophy, his office was almost monastic, its only decoration a huge framed Stars and Stripes flag. His oversized mahogany desk was clear except for an in-tray with just a few sheets of paper waiting for attention. Ezekiel ran a tight ship with no time for extraneous administration.

He sat at the desk and unlocked a hidden drawer underneath, revealing a trove of maps and documents, yellowed with age, handed down from his grandfather, along with the SS ring. They rested upon a Nazi flag, its red and white colors still vivid against the black swastika. It was a risk to keep it here, but when he wavered in his resolve, when the sacrifice ahead seemed too much, Ezekiel found the strength to continue in its stark lines.

The plans had been set in motion almost one hundred years ago, and now finally, they were so close to the beginning of transformational change. Europe had been the center of the world then, but no longer.

What his grandfather's generation had started, he would finish. There would be conflict, and lives would be lost — so many lives. But his experience as a general had taught Ezekiel that no visionary strategy was without cost, and this victory would be worth the sacrifice.

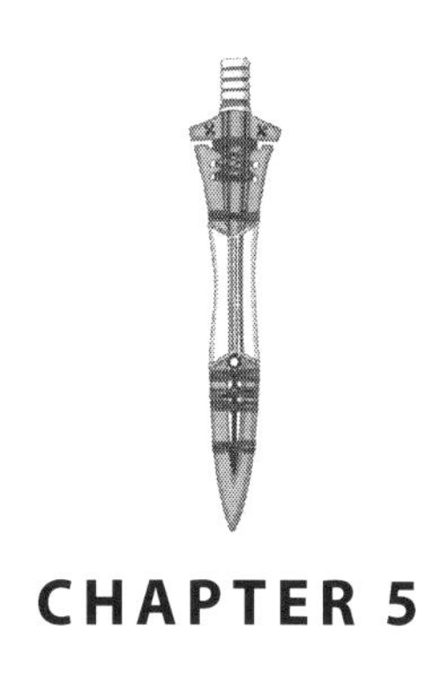

CHAPTER 5

MORGAN PACED UP AND down the pavement in front of Vienna's Monument Against War and Fascism, biting her lip in frustration as she waited for Jake to meet her. It was late now, but the sculpture was dramatically lit, as benefitting a memorial of such historical importance.

Located on Albertinaplatz near the State Opera, the granite blocks of the monument were a brutal reminder of the atrocities of World War II and the Nazi regime, and a warning against the resurgence of such extremism. Half-emerging from the stone, a soldier thrust a knife into the body of a prisoner, as a woman gave birth to a baby under the inhuman gaze of a figure wearing a gas mask. The figures were surrounded by taut chains, razor wire, and the anguished faces of those about to be slaughtered.

The statue — and the city itself — made Morgan uneasy.

Vienna might represent the heights of cultural imperialism and a once great empire that ruled much of Europe, but its dark history lay close to the surface.

Nearly fifty thousand Jews from Vienna had been deported to the camps only hours away from this most refined of cities. Had Morgan lived here with her father back then, she too would have died at the hands of those who viewed her people as less than human.

Decades had passed since that time, but hatred of the Other was once again rising — between nations and religious factions, between political extremes, and even between cultures in the same country. History was circular, and what was once buried would be reborn.

Religious symbols were often used to legitimize the claims of those who sought power, and Morgan wondered whether those who wanted the Spear of Destiny intended to use it to wage a new war.

She cursed her moment of indecision in the State Hall.

When the man with the rune on his neck had jerked away from her in a moment of connection, something inexplicable passed between them. She should have taken that opening. She should have attacked him once more. She might have defeated him, retaken the Spear — and maybe even found out how he knew about her curse.

But as Morgan replayed their fight in her mind, she knew she couldn't have beaten him. His physical strength and speed far exceeded those of any normal man. If she had encountered such a soldier back in the military, before she worked with ARKANE, she would have said he was on some kind of steroids, or enhanced with implants somehow. But after all she had seen in the years since, Morgan wondered if there was something more of the supernatural about him.

His features were fixed in her mind, captured in that moment of connection, a snapshot of the surprise on his face that she replayed over and over again. The cameras in the library or on the streets of Vienna must have caught him leaving the State Hall. With the aid of ARKANE's connections, she would find him again.

She had to find him.

"Morgan." Jake's voice brought her back from the memory, and she turned as he walked around the edge of the monument. "I'm so glad you're safe."

"Is Johannes alright?"

Jake nodded. "The soldiers pursuing us soon peeled off once it was clear you had the Spear."

Morgan shook her head in frustration. "I don't have it anymore. Who the hell were those soldiers, and why didn't we know this would be a combat situation?"

She held back from mentioning her strange connection to the man from the library and his insight into her curse. On previous missions, she would have told Jake everything, but he wouldn't understand this. Besides, she couldn't put into words the way the soldier had made her feel. She would tell Jake later. She was sure they would encounter the unknown fighter again.

Jake held up his hands in mock surrender. "Hey, I know you're angry, and you're right. We should have been better prepared. But I didn't have time to tell you about the letter we found in the Enigma machine before the attack."

He looked up at the carving above him, of the knife thrust into the side of a bound prisoner. "Strange to think it all started here in a time of war."

Morgan frowned. "What did the letter say?"

"It was written by the commander in charge of transporting the Spear from the Hofburg here in Vienna to Nuremberg, Germany, in 1938. It's addressed to Heinrich Himmler himself, Reichsführer of the Schutzstaffel, the SS. He was also the head of the Ahnenerbe, the Nazi group responsible for finding evidence of Germany's global supremacy through archaeological and anthropological expeditions. The letter reports that the Spear had been split into four pieces, as directed. Only one of the original fragments, a long sliver, was forged back into the Spear from the Hofburg."

Morgan couldn't help but smile at Jake's words. The soldier with the rune tattoo only had one piece. The other three were still out there, and she expected he would be on their trail soon enough. She didn't have to find him; he would come to her — if they found the other pieces first.

"Did the letter say where the other fragments were sent?"

Jake shook his head. "That's what we need to find out, but the rest of the commander's papers were taken to Nuremberg, so we'll go there next. It's only a few hours away on the fast train."

Morgan's phone rang, with the tone reserved for her twin sister — who usually texted rather than calling.

Morgan answered quickly. "Faye, what is it? Are you okay?"

Since the mission to recover the Pentecost stones when she had first encountered ARKANE, Morgan was always on the alert for any threat to her family. Faye and her little daughter, Gemma, were the only family Morgan had left. They were everything to her.

Faye's voice was halting, broken with tears. "You need to come home, Morgan. Gemma's in hospital. She collapsed at school."

"What happened?"

"We don't know. She's still unconscious. The doctors are doing all they can but…" Faye sobbed the last words and Morgan's heart wrenched at her sister's pain.

She mentally calculated how fast she could get back to Oxford. "I'm coming. I'll be there later tonight. Stay strong — I'll make sure Gemma gets the best care. I'll be with you soon."

As Morgan ended the call, Jake reached out to touch her arm. "Is it Gemma?"

Morgan nodded. "I have to get back. She's sick, Jake. Really sick."

He opened his arms, and she leaned into his embrace, closing her eyes and breathing in his masculine scent, so reminiscent of pine forests. For just a moment, Morgan lost herself in his strength.

Over the last few years, Jake had been there in her darkest hours, and although he couldn't follow her into the emotional heart of what must come, Morgan knew he was with her in spirit. He had returned for her and Faye and Gemma before, risking an explosion of fire and storm and glass to help save her family. Neither of them would hesitate to run into battle, guns blazing, to protect those they loved, but that didn't help when the enemy was within her niece's tiny body.

Morgan took a deep breath and stepped away. "You go on to Nuremberg and see what you can find. I'll go back to Oxford and help Faye. If I can, I'll join you for whatever comes next."

* * *

A few hours later, Morgan walked through the entrance of the John Radcliffe Hospital in Oxford.

The antiseptic smell made her uneasy, bringing back memories of waking from her own injured oblivion and visiting Jake's comatose body, as well as Father Ben's. The scars she bore were not just etched into her flesh but carved into her soul, and Morgan could almost feel them pulse as she navigated the labyrinthine corridors. As much as she appreciated the work of medical staff, this was not a place she wanted to linger.

She had called ARKANE Director Marietti on the private flight back from Vienna, and he had assured her that Gemma was receiving the best medical care. He assigned a top pediatrician and promised to fund any specialists required. Morgan was grateful for the help, but she had a heavy sense of foreboding as she walked through the corridors, following the brightly colored signs for the children's wing. Death too often followed in her footsteps, and had taken pieces of her heart every time.

"Take me this time," she whispered in a prayer to a god she didn't believe in. "Please, take me."

As Morgan approached the door to the pediatric intensive care unit, her steps slowed. She didn't want to see the reality of what lay ahead. If only she could freeze a happy moment in time — Gemma blowing bubbles in the garden a few weekends ago, her laughter ringing out as Morgan and Faye joined in with delight.

As the memory of laughter faded, Morgan placed her hand on the cold metal of the door handle, a final barrier before the heartache she knew was coming.

She took a deep breath and pushed through.

The hospital room was painted a calm off-white, decorated with cartoon animals, and it looked far too big for the tiny figure lying on her back in the bed. Little Gemma, only five years old, lay still amidst a tangle of tubes and wires, her chest rising and falling with the mechanical rhythm of life support. Her blonde hair lay splayed around her on the pillow; her skin was deathly pale, almost translucent.

Faye sat hunched by Gemma's side, holding the little girl's hand, her features deeply etched with distress.

They were non-identical twins, with Faye's Celtic blonde hair and fair skin reflecting their mother's Welsh heritage, while Morgan's darker skin and brown curls echoed their Sephardic Jewish father. Only their eyes were the same cobalt blue, with a unique violet slash, Morgan's in the right and Faye's in the left.

Their lifestyles were just as different as their looks. Faye was a devoted Christian, a mother to Gemma, and a pillar of their local community in the parish where her husband David was the pastor. The twins had been brought up separately, and Morgan's military experience and now her life as an ARKANE agent could hardly be more different to her sister's.

But none of that mattered.

They were family, and although they had their disagreements, their love for Gemma united them.

Morgan walked around the bed as Faye rose, and they hugged each other tightly. Morgan could sense the tension in her sister's body, and desperately wished she could take that anguish away and bear it on her own shoulders.

They broke apart, and Morgan bent to stroke Gemma's hair and kiss her cheek.

"I'm here, GemGem. I love you. You're going to be okay."

Morgan turned to Faye. "What happened?"

"She was at school. She clutched her chest, went pale, and collapsed. She's been unconscious since. The teacher said she whispered something about her heart before fainting away."

The words sent a chill through Morgan. The Black Anchorite had cursed her with a blood torment for the burning of the heart relic. What if the punishment was not for her, but for the blood of her family? What if her sins were now visited upon Gemma?

Morgan's breath hitched in her chest as the truth of it resonated deep inside. Ancient forces had been loosed that black night and she had clearly not escaped their echo.

"We're still waiting for test results," Faye continued, her voice a mix of hope and despair. She reached out to touch Morgan's hand. "Thank you for arranging the specialists. Everyone is trying their best, and I'm praying for healing and so is the church community. I know God will help us through, for He is faithful and will not give us more than we can bear."

Morgan didn't share Faye's faith, but her years with ARKANE had certainly proved the influence of the supernatural. She was glad her sister had hope, even as she considered that the doctors might not find an answer to Gemma's affliction via medical expertise.

"Where's David?"

"He's gone to get us a change of clothes and some of Gemma's cuddly toys. He'll be back soon."

David Price, Faye's husband, had once been a close

friend to Morgan, in the months after she moved to Oxford to take up a position at the university. The twin sisters had been nearly estranged at the time, and when David almost strayed into being more than a friend, Morgan pulled away. Her relationship with her sister and her niece were the most important thing now.

The door opened, and a doctor entered, examining the computer tablet in his hand with a frown.

"I'm Dr Akintola." He greeted both sisters and bent to examine Gemma, his black hand on hers only emphasizing how pale the little girl was.

He checked the readings on the machines, then added some notes to the tablet records.

"There are a few more tests we need to run. Do you have any family history of heart issues, blood disorders, or… blood cancer?"

Faye gasped at his words and sank back down into the chair by Gemma's side.

"I'm sorry to have to ask, but it might help us figure out what's wrong."

Morgan put her hand on Faye's shoulder, trying to channel strength into her sister. "Our mother died of breast cancer, but there's no history of blood disorders. You'll need to ask David, Gemma's dad, about his background."

Even as she said the words, Morgan knew they wouldn't find anything in the Price family tree. A genetic link might indeed be the key, but it was her bond with Gemma that mattered. They were linked through blood, and the Black Anchorite had somehow reached beyond the grave to strike a blow that hurt far more than any personal injury to herself.

But if this was some kind of supernatural curse, Morgan couldn't tell Faye or the doctors. They must keep working on Gemma from a medical perspective, and she would investigate a cure with the help of ARKANE.

An alarm suddenly blared from the machine next to the bed.

Gemma twitched and seized. Her little body arched up from the bed as she thrashed under the bedding.

Morgan held Faye back as Dr Akintola bent to hold Gemma lightly, so she didn't hurt herself during the seizure.

As the little girl calmed, he adjusted the drip in Gemma's arm. "She's getting worse. I'm going to run some more tests, but we don't have much time to figure this out."

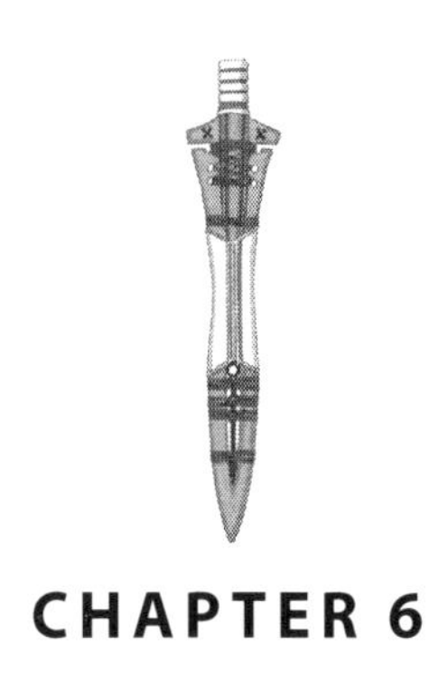

CHAPTER 6

THE STREETS OF THE old town of Nuremberg were quiet as Jake walked up the hill toward the castle. It was late now, and he thought of Morgan back in Oxford with Gemma. He could only hope that she would return and help with the mission because he had a feeling this one would require the pair of them to figure it out.

He had done missions without Morgan before, and he knew they were more effective together — each anticipating the other's need, each trusting the other in even the most dangerous situations.

It was much more than that, of course.

They had come close to taking their relationship into something more than just agents in the field several times, but if they crossed that line, it would change everything. Perhaps it would be a change for the better, but they had both backed away from the edge to preserve what they had.

Perhaps one day it would be too late, but for now, they needed their ARKANE partnership more than ever. Jake worried that Morgan was weakened by the threat of the curse and now Gemma's illness. But, even wounded, she was the only agent he wanted to work with.

As Jake walked on, he saw history evident in the heart of old Nuremberg. The castle walls, brightly illuminated by lights trained on the old stones, loomed above the darkened city. The original fortress dated back to the Middle Ages and its weathered, imposing towers seemed to whisper tales of the Holy Roman Emperors who once resided within its halls. The narrow, cobblestone streets below wound their way through a labyrinth of half-timbered houses, their ancient wooden beams and clay-tiled roofs creating a patchwork of muted color and texture.

Nuremberg had been Hitler's favorite place, and before the war, its medieval architecture and artistic heritage had made it an important cultural hub. The Nazis used it for military rallies, and the Führer had given many of his famous speeches here, intending the city to be of great future importance. But this was also where the Nuremberg Trials were held to prosecute the defeated Nazis for their atrocities, an attempt to redress the balance of dark history.

Much of the city, including the Imperial Castle, had been rebuilt after Allied bombing raids reduced it to rubble. Skilled architects used the principle of 'creative conservation' to restore the city to its medieval glory, reusing much of the old material. The work had taken many years, but the vision had finally been fulfilled. It was here, hidden beneath the restored castle's watchful gaze, that Jake found the entrance to the Historischer Kunstbunker.

Discreet and unassuming, the doorway was a portal to a world far removed from the modern city, and as Jake approached, a middle-aged woman stepped from the shadows.

She was tall and angular, her grey hair pixie cropped, a long fleece coat wrapped around her, secured tightly with a belt against the winter cold. She reached out a hand.

"I'm Lotte. I'll escort you into the bunker tonight."

Jake shook her hand. "Thank you. I'm sorry it's late, but I need to see the room where the imperial regalia and the Heilige Lanze were kept."

"Of course, follow me."

Lotte pulled out a set of keys and unlocked the massive door. She waved Jake inside, followed him in, and locked the door behind them.

They stood in darkness for a moment, and Jake breathed in the air. It had a cool earthiness with a mineral edge, with no trace of the beer that was once stored in these cellars.

Lotte flicked on a light, and a series of dim bulbs flared along the corridor as it sloped into the gloom.

The walls were rough, hewn from the bedrock upon which Nuremberg was built, and framed posters from the wartime era, now yellowed with age, hung at intervals. They glorified the city's efforts to defend its cultural treasures from those who attacked sovereign Germany. Those who were now portrayed as victorious Allies in the annals of history were the enemy to those huddled here as bombs rained down overhead.

Your perspective differed depending on what side of a conflict you were on. As a white South African, Jake understood how the place and time of one's birth affected the trajectory of a life.

A drug-fueled gang, high on meth, had hacked apart his parents and younger sister back in Walkerville near Johannesburg years ago. While he had avenged their murders, he later realized it was just another violent act in a blood feud played out over generations, incited by racial hatred on both sides. As soon as one group saw the other as less than human, conflict erupted and could only end in destruction, as it had here so many times in human history.

The corridor opened up into a wider chamber, and Lotte stopped to explain the machinery that lay rusting in the shadows. There were pumps and air conditioning for water and fresh air, as well as heating to keep the temperature at the right level to protect the precious relics and artwork once stored here.

She pointed out some of the structural elements. "The city's engineers devised packing methods to absorb shock waves from bombing. They used layers of sandbags and wooden frames, and even suspended the more delicate items to prevent damage from vibration."

Jake shook his head in wonder. "They really cared about these cultural objects, right? Shame about all the people whose lives were lost."

Lotte nodded. "Indeed. But that is the eternal quandary of those who see works of art as precious beyond the value of human life. Some objects stored here were centuries old and treasured for generations."

She led Jake into a storage room, empty but for pictures of what had been stored there. "This chamber once held *Der Sachsenspiegel*, a medieval law book from around 1220 that illustrated the legal system of the Holy Roman Empire."

She shone her torch into an alcove reinforced with wooden beams. "And here lay *Die Manessische Liederhandschrift*, a collection of Minnesang poetry, testament to the Germanic spirit and artistic expression of the thirteenth century."

She spun around once more and led Jake into a high-ceilinged chamber off the main section. It was empty, with a huge black-and-white photo at the end portraying life-size sculptures of saints in billowing robes.

Jake walked closer to examine it. "These figures are so intricate." He looked around at the empty space. "It's strange to imagine them down here years ago."

"They're statues from the Krakauer Marienaltar, the Gothic masterpiece dismantled and brought here for protection from Kraków, Poland by the Nazis. Whatever the controversy over the looting, the altar was indeed protected when much that lay above ground all over Europe was destroyed by years of war. Despite the intentions of those who built this place, I consider it a light in the darkness of that period of history."

Jake nodded. "I'm South African, and now I live in England and fight for what is left of its values. I understand the burden of a country whose history we might want to disown sometimes. All we can do is act as we wished our ancestors had done."

Lotte smiled. "I'm glad you see it that way. Many of us cannot bear to see the vibrant modern country we love still associated with such dark times."

They walked on past two enormous steel doors, reinforced with cross-beams next to an open hatch leading into the guard's quarters.

"There were four police officers on duty in rotation here. Other beer cellars throughout the city protected people as the bombs fell, but this one was only for the most precious artworks. The officers slept in there."

Jake stepped into the room, curious about how the men lived as bombs rained down overhead. It was sparsely furnished with a wooden table and bench, next to bunk beds. A dusty old telephone was attached to the wall, the only line to the outside world.

The walls were stained with the passage of time, hung with faded photographs and documents, remnants of propaganda that once fueled the war machine. Jake imagined the guards poring over them, searching for conviction in the lines of text and images. Were they proud protectors of this plundered history, or did they sense the shadows of lives torn apart above?

There was a dichotomy about the bunker. It was at once a sanctuary and a tomb — a safe haven for priceless art and religious relics, but also evidence of theft, looting, and violence. The dust of memory stirred with his breath, and it seemed to Jake that the ghosts of the dead still lingered in the shadows.

He shivered and turned to Lotte. "Can you take me to where they kept the imperial regalia and the Heilige Lanze?"

"Of course, it's just a little way ahead."

They rounded a corner of the narrow bunker and entered a smaller space walled with concrete blocks interspersed with extra insulating material. Wooden planks lined the floor, and functional brickwork arched overhead. There were informational placards around the walls, one displaying life-size photos of the imperial regalia and the Spear that Jake had last seen in Vienna. It felt far more like a museum space than the more personal bunk room, and Jake wondered if the guards had come in here to wonder at the treasures they guarded.

"This is where the sacred imperial objects were kept, right until the Allies began their final push into Germany. You might have heard about the Monuments Men? There was a film with George Clooney and Matt Damon about them a while back."

Jake shrugged. "I haven't seen it, but I vaguely remember the details. The Americans who recovered much of the stolen Nazi art, right?"

Lotte pointed at one of the placards. "Yes, they saved thousands of pieces from destruction or disappearance, returning them to ensure that future generations could appreciate our shared cultural heritage. This was just one place they found stolen artifacts. There were thousands of treasures in mines across Germany, like the salt mine at Altaussee, which housed special objects Hitler wanted for his Führermuseum. But of course, that was never built."

She pointed at another placard. "This Congress Hall was also planned as a grand complex designed to house the imperial regalia and the Heilige Lanze. They were more than just historical artifacts to Hitler. They were symbols of power which would legitimize him with the authority of the Holy Roman Emperors."

Jake bent to examine the image. Beneath the architectural plans, there was a photo of Adolf Hitler himself standing before a glass case, gazing inside at the imperial regalia and the Spear of Destiny. He had his hands folded in front of him and he bent his head in reverence, lost in thought.

It was strange to witness such a moment through time. Perhaps if Hitler had possessed the entire Spear, rather than just a fragment, its power might have changed the course of the war. Was someone now seeking the Spear in order to pursue such a dark course again?

Jake turned back to Lotte. "After the Regalia were recovered, who verified the Spear of Destiny? How did they know it was the real thing amidst all the chaos?"

Lotte sighed. "The end of the war brought a fog of uncertainty. Despite the best efforts of the Monuments Men and the Allied forces, many artifacts were lost, stolen, or hidden away. Ensuring the authenticity of each was a monumental task."

She paused, her gaze drifting back to the plans of the Congress Hall. "Some items were easier to identify than others, but the Spear… its history, enhanced by legend, makes it unique and sought by many. There are no records I know of around the verification of what left Vienna, what arrived here, and what was returned to the Hofburg again after the war. There are photos, of course, but they're black and white. It's hard to tell what's real from such images."

Lotte turned to walk out of the bunker and then spun back around. "You know, there is an obscure book theorizing that Himmler had an exact copy made of the Lance before it even arrived here. The American author, Howard Buechner, was a colonel and a medical doctor who also wrote about the horrors he witnessed liberating the Dachau concentration camp, so he has credibility as a source. And of course, it's well known that Himmler was more deeply involved in the occult than Hitler was. He funded much… unusual research under the banner of the Ahnenerbe, the department for Ancestral Heritage."

Jake raised an eyebrow as he joined her by the doorway. "Interesting. Where might Himmler have taken this copy of the Spear?"

"Wewelsburg Castle would be the most obvious place. It was Himmler's intended 'center of the world,' where it's rumored he led occult ceremonies for his elite SS soldiers. It's only about four hours' drive north of here."

"That's useful," Jake said. "I appreciate your help, and thanks for coming out this late."

Lotte led the way back through the bunker complex toward the entrance.

It was the early hours of the morning now, and there was little more to be gained in these halls of history. There had been no death down here, and religious artifacts had been stacked in the bunker rather than gassed and stripped bodies, but Jake still felt the chill of the tomb, and he longed to escape into the fresh air.

They passed stark, black-and-white photographs documenting Nuremberg's fate during and after the Allied bombings. Each image told a story of devastation, hundreds of years of human creation razed to the ground. The St Lorenz Church, its once majestic spire reduced to rubble. The Frauenkirche with its partially collapsed roof, and the Kaiserburg, which had stood as a symbol of the city's imperial significance, all bearing the scars of war.

Further down the corridor, other photos showed the painstaking reconstruction of these iconic landmarks, brick by brick, until the city's historical heart beat once more, and the continent struggled back to life.

Lotte stopped in front of one photo, showing survivors rebuilding the city. "The wheel of history turns again, and you and I — descendants of enemies on opposite sides — can be friends once more. When I worry about war rising again, it gives me hope. No matter what comes, at some point it will end, and the lines on our maps will be redrawn once more."

Jake nodded. “Indeed, and we can only hope we’ll still be here to see what comes after.”

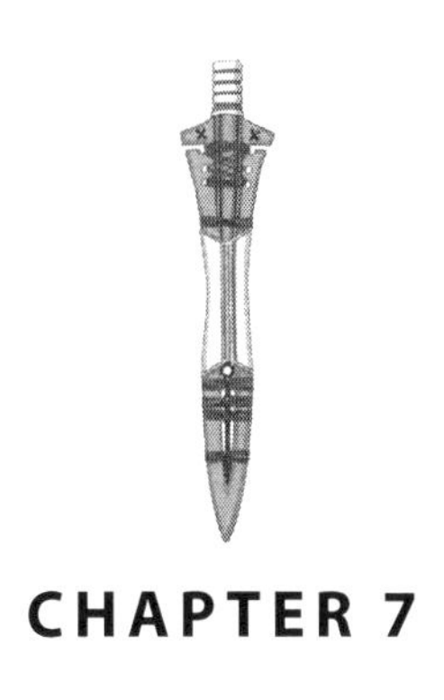

CHAPTER 7

MORGAN WALKED OUT OF the hospital into the winter dawn, the cold air helping to clear her head as the doctor's words about Gemma's condition rang in her ears.

The moon was still visible even as streaks of ashen-rose sunlight split the dark clouds overhead. It was a moment of calm before the day began and the city bustled into life once more, but Morgan found it hard to consider what normal life might look like right now.

She had left Faye sleeping in the chair next to her daughter's bed, and while she hoped the rest might help her sister cope, Morgan couldn't stay there doing nothing. Perhaps the curse of the Black Anchorite was not responsible for Gemma's illness, but it was too much of a coincidence to dismiss altogether. While the doctors did their best work on the medical side, she would investigate the supernatural possibilities, and there was only one person she trusted to help with that.

Morgan set out for the short walk across Oxford to the Museum of Natural History, which housed one of the ARKANE regional hubs in the levels beneath. The route cut through a residential area and then opened out into Marston Meadows, where cycle paths and walking trails bisected fields with tall trees and thick hedgerows.

Birdsong pierced the air with the sweet notes of a dawn chorus, but all Morgan could hear was the sound of time passing too quickly as Gemma lay suffering.

She lengthened her stride, overtaking the early morning dog walkers at a brisk pace. But as she wound her way through the paths to the museum, Morgan suddenly got the sensation of being watched.

She spun around, looking down into a darkened lane that branched off from the main path, half-expecting — half-wanting — to see a figure with a rune tattoo on his neck emerge from the shadows.

But no one was there, and she saw nothing she could pinpoint as the source of her unease.

A gust of chill wind blew, and she shivered, pulling her coat more tightly around her. Morgan thought of the soldier from Vienna. Could his team be following her, or was her disquiet just lack of sleep, concern for Gemma, and fear of the curse? She had to pull herself together or she would be no use to her family, or to Jake and ARKANE.

Morgan took one last look behind and quickened her pace, soon emerging from the back of Linacre College into the maze of university scientific buildings.

There were departments here for theoretical chemistry and pathogen research, as well as the more established disciplines of biology and biochemistry. She hurried past them all, turning a final corner to reach the Museum of Natural History.

Rays of early sun painted the sky in hues of coral and gold, casting the Gothic Revival facade of the museum into sharp relief. With its central tower, arched windows, and elegant stone architecture, the museum could have been a monastery or some other religious building in another age. But here and now, science was worshipped just as much as any god.

Morgan walked up the steps through the grand archway

carved with entwined flora and fauna, and clicked her pass against the electronic scanner.

Most who worked at the museum thought the academic side of the ARKANE Institute had a small office out the back, unaware of the levels below the museum, where groundbreaking science blurred with the edge of the supernatural.

Morgan's footsteps echoed in the great hall as she hurried across. Its expansive glass roof allowed morning light to pierce the gloom, casting shadows around the skeletons of dinosaurs frozen in time, jaws wide, ready for attack.

The beauty of the Victorian design with its slender columns rising to filigree-decorated capitals usually stirred Morgan to a sense of awe at what humans could create, but today she couldn't shake her melancholy. The museum, for all its evidence of enlightenment, was a reminder of the relentless march of time that left only dust in its wake.

She walked through to the back of the hall and into the Pitt Rivers Museum beyond. It housed the collection of a Victorian explorer and archaeologist whose methods of obtaining the precious objects were now under scrutiny. But the place was a marvel for curious minds and Morgan hoped that the unique elements of the collection might remain, despite the controversy.

The Pitt Rivers was a labyrinth of wonder, each closely packed glass case a portal to another time, an insight into another culture's deepest beliefs and fears. The smell of polished wood and mineral oil from the display cases mingled with the mustiness of old bones and the faint trace of damp stone as Morgan walked through. She had always been drawn to the higgledy-piggledy arrangement of the museum, where chaos ordered itself into a strange harmony. It was much more to her liking than the ornate and precisely ordered collections in Vienna's Hofburg.

There were many religious aspects to the collection. A statue of Shiva Nataraja, with its many hands and fierce beauty, stood poised to leap into battle against tribal gods from distant lands. A portrait of a Christian martyr's twisted agony stood beside ceremonial knives used for blood rites in the South Pacific.

Tiny handwritten notes accompanied every artifact, blending the mundane and the mystical. Each piece spoke of the thin veil between the known and the unknowable that perhaps Victorian explorers understood far more easily than researchers of the secular present.

Many of the artifacts in the museum were actually fakes, with the genuine items studied in the ARKANE labs below, some a source of ancient power under investigation. While Morgan had once doubted the validity of such supernatural power, she had seen enough during her ARKANE missions that she now accepted science could not account for everything. Sometimes, the answer lay beyond rationality — and she could only hope that might help Gemma now.

Morgan wound her way through the display cases until she reached a flight of stairs and descended into the crypt. There was a large wooden door in one corner, which looked like a discreet store cupboard.

She swiped her card once more and emerged onto a small balcony overlooking the five levels of ARKANE labs below.

Large windows opened onto a light well, revealing glass-walled labs below with long tables and equipment for varying kinds of analysis. With one brief glance, Morgan spotted an ancient manuscript, an intricately carved stone depiction of a forgotten god, and a metal curse tablet in the rooms below. She fleetingly wondered what stories they might tell and what wonders they might reveal — but as ever, there wasn't enough time in the world to pursue all the mysteries that lay even just within this building.

While the primary ARKANE complex lay below Trafalgar Square in London, this Oxford regional hub was important for the analysis of the treasures held within the fabled city of spires. Although the labs were mostly empty at this early hour, during the day investigators worked to fathom ancient secrets, with the soft hum of advanced machinery mingling with the timeless whispers of ancient relics.

Morgan headed down the stairs to the first level and entered one of the conference rooms.

Martin Klein, ARKANE's Head Archivist, sat engrossed in his laptop, his fingertips flying across the keyboard as he stared unblinking at the screen, his head tilted to one side. Martin's shock of blond hair was even more ruffled than usual, evidence that he had been pondering a difficult problem, while his glasses, with their wire-thin frames, perched precariously on the bridge of his nose.

"Hi, Martin," Morgan said softly, not wanting to startle him.

He stood abruptly, pushing his chair back with a metallic scrape. He bounced up and down on the balls of his feet, bobbling and weaving a little.

"I'm so sorry about Gemma, but I think I have something for you to look at based on her test results."

When ARKANE Director Marietti had assigned the top pediatricians to Gemma's case, Morgan made sure all her records were copied on to Martin. He didn't do small talk, but his social awkwardness was a small price to pay for the depth of insight he provided, and labels didn't matter when he was so valuable to the team.

Martin's mind worked differently. He perceived patterns in chaos where others could see nothing and he had built a custom artificial intelligence engine to find deeper connections based on the millions of scanned manuscripts and images that ARKANE collected. In collaboration, the man and his machine were a dance of neurons and code, sparking off each other to detect new secrets in the fabric of history and the weave of the supernatural — and perhaps, Morgan hoped, in the twisting nature of DNA and human blood.

"What have you found?" She walked around to look at Martin's laptop screen, careful to keep her distance in respect for his aversion to touch.

"I found some unusual markers in Gemma's blood." He clicked through to images of cells stained with purple and annotated with code. "These same markers have been discovered in the blood of those with stigmata and other religiously induced wounds. I'm also researching evidence around exorcism-related injury."

Morgan stifled a gasp at his words. "What do you mean?"

"There are cases where physical wounds appear on the bodies of those considered possessed." Martin frowned. "Of course, many would say these are psychosomatic, that the brain causes them to occur and that it has nothing to do with the demonic."

Morgan took a breath as she considered his words. She couldn't bear the idea of Gemma suffering in this way, but she had to face the possibility of it being true. "Perhaps there's something truly ancient at work and it's a genuine phenomenon. What could heal such a wound?"

Martin pulled up images of several ancient books. "We finally have all the manuscripts scanned from the citadel of the Black Anchorite, recovered after your last mission. There are lists of religious relics that have healing properties and, of course, the items from the Passion of Christ are considered the most powerful. Thorns from the crown, slivers of wood from the True Cross, a piece of cloth from the Shroud—"

"What about the Spear of Longinus, the Spear of Destiny?" Morgan interrupted.

"Yes, of course. According to legend, the blood of Christ trickled down the spear and healed the eyesight of the centurion, Longinus, so any of these sacred objects might help Gemma. The question is where the genuine relics might be. Most scattered around Christendom are clearly fakes."

Morgan paced up and down as she considered the current

mission. "We think the Spear held in the Vienna treasury was at least a part of the real one, so more fragments are out there. I'll find them, Martin, but you need to figure out how they might help Gemma."

He nodded. "Of course. I've branched the algorithm to examine patterns within apocryphal texts banned by the early Church, ancient medical treatises by doctors who believed in the supernatural, cross-referencing to modern hematological papers and unpublished clinical trials."

Morgan couldn't help but smile at Martin's intense drive to help her niece. "Thank you. I didn't understand most of that, but I trust you'll find something by the time I get hold of the Spear."

Morgan's phone rang, its tone loud in the quiet of the lab.

She pulled it from her pocket to see Jake's name on the screen. She answered quickly.

"Hi, Jake. You're on speaker. I'm at the ARKANE Oxford labs with Martin."

"Morning, Spooky." Martin's affectionate nickname was based on how often the Archivist came up with such extraordinary insights, and he smiled at his friend's voice.

"Morning, Jake. What news?"

"There was nothing definitive about the Spear in the Nuremberg bunker, but now I'm heading north to Himmler's castle at Wewelsburg, which has occult links with the Spear."

"I'm coming," Morgan said quickly, her decision made before she could even think about it rationally. "I can't do anything for Gemma here. I can fly into… wait a minute."

Martin checked the details on his laptop. "There's a tiny airfield at Paderborn near Wewelsburg. You can take a private Cessna from Oxford airport. It's only a few hours."

"If you leave soon, you'll beat me there," Jake said, a wry smile in his tone. "It will be good to have you with me. You're more of an expert in the occult than I am, for sure."

"I'll text you my travel details and see you in a few hours."

Morgan ended the call, then turned to Martin. "Can you send me all the details you can find — conspiracy theory or historical fact — about Wewelsburg?"

"Of course, I'll set that going now." Martin began typing again, his fingers moving so fast across the keys, they seemed to blur into the machine.

Morgan walked toward the door. She had time to go back to her little house in the Jericho area of Oxford and pick up a change of clothes before flying again, but she still wondered about the soldier in Vienna. Knowing more about him would help the mission.

"I need one more thing."

Martin looked up. "Of course. Anything."

"The soldiers who invaded the treasury in Vienna. Do you have anything on them yet?"

Martin opened another screen and pulled up the security footage from the Schatzkammer. Morgan watched as the military team moved swiftly through the museum, then as she and Jake hauled Johannes out of the room housing the imperial regalia, before the soldiers entered. She recognized the stature of the leader, but the angle of the camera was too high to show any detail.

"They didn't have any insignia." Morgan pointed at the screen. "But that man had a tattoo on his neck. Some kind of rune. He had an American accent and he was…"

As her voice trailed off, Martin frowned at her hesitation. "He was what?"

Morgan shook her head. "I don't know. Maybe unusually strong. And he could sense what I was about to do before I did it. There was something about him. Do you have footage from the State Hall in the Library?"

"No, the equipment had been damaged beforehand, maybe deliberately. I'll try to narrow it down and send you some photos of active military officers and militia to see if you recognize him."

Morgan nodded, the man's face blazing in her memory. "Okay, that'll have to do."

"Be careful over there, Morgan." Martin swung his screen around to reveal an image of a black mosaic set into the floor of a circular hall.

It was a Black Sun, a Schwarze Sonne, with twelve radial sig runes, like those used in the insignia of the SS. A symbol that evoked terror even generations later for its association with the death camps that tortured and murdered millions.

Martin reached out a hand, his fingers hovering just over Morgan's arm, touching the air as another would caress skin, a gesture that was as close as he ever got to physical touch. "There's darkness in this history, and I fear you are stumbling into something that should not be awakened."

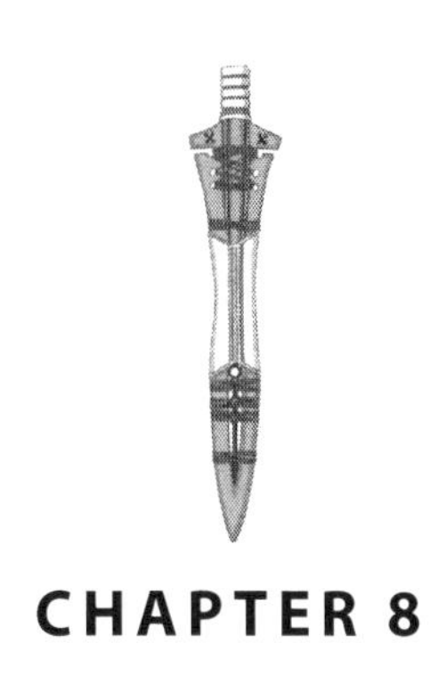

CHAPTER 8

GABRIEL BLACKTHORN DROVE THE last few miles through the northern edge of the Blue Ridge Mountains, skirting the border of the Shenandoah National Park. The majestic range, part of the Appalachian Mountains, stretched to the horizon, and he rolled down the window to breathe in the crisp air. The scent of pine mingled with the faint hint of wood smoke curling from distant cabins, like the ones he explored in this area as a kid.

He had wandered alone, always alone. It was easier that way.

Gabriel had always known he was adopted, even though his devout Christian family treated him the same as their other children. He had never truly felt at ease with them, hiding his more… unusual skills so as not to stand out. But here alone in the woods, he could be himself.

He could run and hunt and climb with no one to comment on how fast he was, or how he could hear the slightest animal sound from miles away, or how he smelled things beyond normal human comprehension. Out here in the rugged wilderness, Gabriel had found home, and later, he'd found it once more with General Stronghold and Jericho Command.

After the long flight back from Europe, it was good to

be back on US soil. The chill wind carried the crisp scent of snow from the mountain peaks, and the moon, nearly full, cast a pale light over the landscape, transforming the trees into silver sculptures, ethereal and otherworldly.

Out of the corner of his eye, Gabriel thought he saw strange creatures soaring high, with fangs and claws, and leathery wings spread wide. There was much he sensed beyond the physical realm, but over the years, he had learned to tune it out and certainly never reveal it to others. But after the encounter in the Vienna library, he wondered if there were others like him, after all.

His combat team had traveled from the airport back to Jericho Command base in a bigger van, but Gabriel needed some time alone. The mission hadn't gone exactly to plan, but General Stronghold would still have his Spear. The precious relic lay next to him on the passenger seat, wrapped in layers of silk and locked into a fireproof case.

But it wasn't the Spear that haunted Gabriel, it was the woman he fought in the library.

She clearly had military experience, and he recognized her skill in Krav Maga. He had not wanted to hurt her, so he moderated his true strength, but she certainly held her own in the fight. Her eyes were extraordinary, but it was the depth in them rather than the color he remembered so vividly. When his gaze met hers, Gabriel felt a connection that went beyond the physical. When he touched her skin, the electricity almost burned him.

She had brushed up against true darkness somehow, and it had left a shadow in her blood that called to him. Gabriel didn't know why, or what it meant, but whatever happened with this mission, he was determined to find her again.

He rounded the last few sweeping turns through the forest and passed through a hidden security zone, his biometrics scanned multiple times along the final kilometers, allowing him access.

The Jericho Command militia base was positioned at the foot of a steep mountain, camouflaged by the forest. It was a warren of low exterior buildings and excavated cave chambers that extended over many kilometers. While a black ops government department controlled most of the units, Gabriel's team reported to General Stronghold, who now directed the more… unconventional missions. The base was only a few hours from Washington, DC and Gabriel expected the general to retrieve the Spear later tonight.

Gabriel was loyal to the general and, for much of his career, it had been unquestioned allegiance. He owed much to General Stronghold's personal interest in his direction. But if he was honest, Gabriel had started to sense the collision of mighty forces ahead, a preternatural discernment that a bigger conflict was coming — with the general at its heart. His team at Jericho Command would therefore be at the center of whatever was to come and that disturbed him. He had heard reports of the Capitol rally. Talk of war and conflict and lives lost even within the borders of the USA. Distant thunderclouds were gathering, coming closer and threatening to break at any moment. He could not go on for much longer without questioning the general's plan, but for now at least, he would fulfill his orders.

Gabriel headed through the exterior security perimeter checks and parked outside the spartan living quarters of the active teams on site. He left his personal bag in his room and headed for the training area, carrying the Spear with him in its fireproof case. The best thing to dissolve the tension in his body post-flight was a workout, and it might be the only way to clear his mind of the woman from the library.

Gabriel climbed the stairs to the general's office, which overlooked the massive training hall below. An eye scan and biometric data allowed him inside to the inner sanctum, but Gabriel didn't linger.

Two groups of soldiers sparred in a flurry of blows below

as their team shouted encouragement. He belonged down there with them, not up here in an office.

He set the case down on the general's desk and hurried back to the sparring level below.

Gabriel paused at the perimeter.

His soldiers — his warriors — were engaged in a simulation of battle, their bodies moving in a dance of controlled aggression under a huge Stars and Stripes flag. The sharp clang of steel against steel, the dull thud of fists against flesh, and the sporadic crack of gunfire filled the air. The sound of Jericho Command in action.

Gabriel watched the fluid movements of each man as he trained, each known to him over countless missions. They were his family now, bound not by blood but by a shared purpose, and a belief in the righteousness of their missions.

He stepped forward into the ring, and a palpable shift swept through the group of gathered soldiers.

Two men stopped sparring mid-fight, turning to nod respectfully at Gabriel as he stood, his hard-muscled body tense and ready for action.

"Alright, who's up?"

The two men already in the ring glanced at each other and then crouched, circling in opposite directions, choosing to fight their commander together instead of each other.

They attacked in a flurry of aggression.

Gabriel darted between his opponents with a grace that belied his powerful frame, each strike a harmonious blend of combat techniques refined by years of relentless training and active missions.

"You must be tired, Gabe. Is that all you've got?" one man taunted.

Gabriel answered with a swift, precise move that unbalanced him, sending him tumbling to the mat.

The other soldier darted in with an aggressive strike.

Gabriel effortlessly dodged. "Nice try, but watch your left flank."

His supernatural senses allowed him to perceive the subtle shifts in his opponents. He smelled their sweat and determination, along with the metallic hint of blood from earlier bouts. He heard the rasp of a foot on the mat sweeping sideways, the whisper of air against skin, and the pulsating heartbeats of his adversaries.

One man tagged out and two more joined the first.

Now fighting three men, Gabriel's movements became a blur. He was everywhere at once, his strikes a faint promise of what he could truly unleash.

"Better," he acknowledged after a particularly well-executed counter from one soldier. "Use your environment more. Anticipate."

As he spun around with a back kick, driving one of his assailants away, a sudden, unbidden memory pierced Gabriel's concentration.

The woman in the library, her determined gaze shadowed by the weight of cursed blood, flashed before him. The scent of her skin mingled with the leather-bound books rose up, pulling him momentarily from the reality of the ring to questions of his lineage and the dark mystery that flowed through his veins.

One of his soldiers, seizing the unexpected opportunity, landed a solid punch to Gabriel's midsection.

The impact was a sharp, jarring return to reality, the sound of the blow echoing unnaturally loud in his ears.

A collective intake of breath echoed in the room.

But the moment of surprise was fleeting.

Gabriel's reaction was swift, a storm unleashed. Anger, not at the soldier but at his own momentary weakness, fueled his movements.

His counterattack was a whirlwind, each strike a declaration of his dominion. The surrounding air thrummed, his earlier lapse transformed into a display of terrifying efficiency. His fists found their marks with ruthless precision, a clear message of dominance to all who watched.

When the three opponents lay bruised and panting on the mats around him, Gabriel held up a hand to stop the session, as sweat dripped from his body.

"If you gain an advantage, however slight, press the attack," he growled. "Or your enemy may regain their focus and finish you."

Gabriel held out a hand to one man, helping him to his feet as the others hobbled off.

"Good work tonight, all of you. Now rest and get some sleep. Our next mission starts tomorrow."

The soldiers filed out, and within minutes Gabriel stood alone in the center of the sparring ring, his breathing steady once more.

The focus of extreme exertion was a blessed escape from the turmoil of his thoughts, but now they rushed back in. He had chased away the question of his true lineage for so long, sublimating it with endless missions before crashing into dreamless, exhausted sleep.

But now the woman from Vienna had awakened a need to know more. Could she be the key to discovering who he really was?

Gabriel felt a prickle of awareness.

He was being watched.

He spun around and looked up at the wide glass window overlooking the hall. General Stronghold raised a hand in greeting, and after a beat, Gabriel returned the gesture before heading to the showers.

* * *

As Ezekiel watched Gabriel stride away with the grace of a predator after feeding, he wondered how long he could keep his finest soldier in check, especially as the plan was now starting to unfold.

He had directed Gabriel's course since birth, and made

sure the child he once was had been raised in a strict Christian home in the USA. The discipline of the military had kept him occupied over the decades since, but suddenly Ezekiel sensed a new unrest in Gabriel and that was a danger, indeed. It was imperative that he not discover the secret of his bloodline. If revealed, the knowledge could shatter the man he had become.

Sending Gabriel on a mission to retrieve the Spear had been a dangerous choice. Ezekiel usually sent the commander on missions far away from the dark strands of history in that area of Europe. But Gabriel's team was the most effective, and Ezekiel needed the Spear urgently in order to start the countdown to its activation.

And here it was.

He walked over to the desk and opened the fireproof case. Inside was a bundle of blue silk. He lifted it out and carefully unwrapped the Spear until he held the relic in one hand.

The metal was cold and yet, was there a jolt of spiritual power lying dormant, waiting to be unleashed at the right time?

He reached beneath his black shirt to touch the warmth of the death's head ring that bound him to the past. His grandfather had been part of Himmler's secret Ahnenerbe elite, those in the inner circle who understood that only supernatural powers channelled through ancient relics could secure the dominion of a Thousand Year Reich. Hitler had become increasingly dependent on military conquest, believing that human soldiers could achieve what Himmler knew was impossible.

By splitting the Spear into pieces, Himmler hoped to preserve it for a leader who was willing to channel its power for victory in both human and spiritual realms. But over the generations, despite trying different paths to power, the descendants of the Ahnenerbe had failed.

Until now.

It had taken many years of sacrifice and strategic positioning, but at last Ezekiel could see the path to power, and he was the perfect candidate to wield the Spear.

The time had come for the pieces to be reunited again, but the location of some fragments were lost to history. His grandfather knew of this one, embedded into the Lance and kept in plain sight in the Schatzkammer of Vienna. There was one more secured by a man of integrity in a symbolic location, which Ezekiel would send Gabriel for next. But the other two fragments were missing.

Ezekiel bent his head and prayed, asking God for guidance at this junction of history, for His help in finding the other pieces. Surely it was the right time for them to emerge.

The power of the Spear of Destiny would take a resurgent United States into the future, cleansed of sin and weakness, returned to divine favor.

He also prayed for Gabriel and the soldiers who followed him to remain faithful to the cause, without the burden of knowing what must follow. He had to keep the secret from Gabriel until the greater truth was revealed. Then it wouldn't matter anymore as a new Thousand Year Reich would be ushered in, here, in the land of the free.

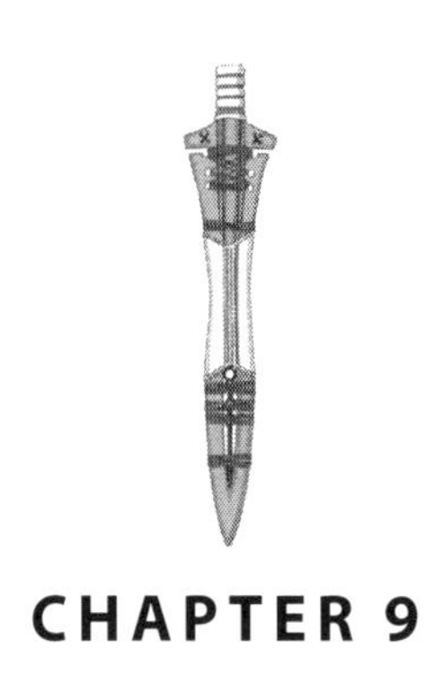

CHAPTER 9

IT WAS A SHORT ride from the airport to Wewelsburg village, and Morgan gazed out the window as Jake drove along the undulating roads leading to the castle.

She was glad to be on the move, and although every kilometer across the German landscape took her further away from Gemma, she could only hope it would bring her closer to some answers.

They rounded a corner, and the imposing castle came into view. It stood on a rocky promontory, surrounded by trees overlooking the serene Alme Valley. It had an unusual triangular form, with three corner towers and high brick walls.

Built in the seventeenth century, the castle was originally intended as a secondary residence for the Prince Bishops of Paderborn, and later co-opted by Himmler for the SS. During the last days of the war, the defeated soldiers had almost completely destroyed it, but some of the structure had been rebuilt and was now a museum.

There were understandable legal restrictions in Germany around the use of Nazi symbols, as well as laws forbidding denial of the Holocaust, so access to certain areas of the castle was strictly controlled. ARKANE Director Marietti had called in a favor with the Minister of State for Culture and the Media, so Morgan and Jake would have access to those parts usually off limits.

They pulled up in front of the castle and approached the heavy main door.

It creaked open as they walked up the steps, and as Morgan and Jake entered the hallway, a man stepped forward to greet them.

He appeared like an extension of the castle itself, as if hewn from the same austere stone. He was tall and imposing, yet there was a stoop to his shoulders, a curvature that hinted at years steeped in the same heavy history. His face was angular, the sharp lines of his jaw and cheekbones mirroring the geometric precision of the castle's architecture.

"Welcome to Wewelsburg. I'm Klaus Oster, head curator. I received your permissions. Everything is in order. Please follow me."

The curator's voice was like the rustle of old parchment, with a scratchy timbre that echoed in the stone halls. Morgan gave a wry smile at his brusque introduction as they followed him into the long corridor ahead.

They walked through the open halls, now transformed into different exhibit areas for varying aspects of the museum.

The Historical Museum of the Bishopric of Paderborn dominated one wing, maintained with rooms in the style of the aristocrats who once lived here. Another wing held an educational memorial of the war years, featuring back-lit cases with stark black and white photos of Nazi atrocities, and boards documenting the ideology and terror of the SS.

Morgan stopped in front of one image, a plan of the Niederhagen concentration camp and pictures of its liberation.

There were only a few names that echoed through history — Auschwitz, Dachau, Birkenau — but at the height of Nazi power, there had been twenty-three major camps, and perhaps a thousand satellite camps.

Niederhagen had been relatively small, and those interned here were used as slave labor for Himmler's castle developments. Nearly four thousand people had passed through the camp, and in keeping with the Nazi principle of "extermination through labor," almost a third died or were executed before liberation. The camp even required its own crematorium to handle the number of deaths at the facility.

Morgan tried to imagine what it must have been like to work in the castle under the eyes of Himmler himself. She shuddered as she imagined how much more scientific the regime's destruction could have been with the purity of race assessed by modern genetic sequencing. Blood revealed all, and certainly Morgan would have been taken along with her father.

Klaus turned to look back. "There is little time before the museum opens. We must proceed to the chamber at once. You may visit the museum again after your allocated time slot in the crypt."

He hurried them on, and Jake raised an eyebrow at the curator's blunt manner. His corkscrew scar twisted as he made a face at Klaus's back, and Morgan appreciated the moment of levity in this dark place where the ashes of the dead seemed to linger in the atmosphere.

Klaus stopped in front of a doorway in the North Tower and turned to face them. He stood taller now, and there was a deference in his voice.

"This is the Obergruppenführersaal, the Hall of the Supreme Leaders." He pointed above to a Latin inscription. "*Domus mea domus orationis vocabitur*. My house shall be called a house of prayer."

Morgan replied in a low voice laced with steel. "Perhaps they should have included the rest of that verse from Isaiah chapter fifty-six: 'their burnt offerings and sacrifices will be accepted on my altar.' Himmler certainly presided over both."

Klaus didn't reply to her barely restrained anger. He merely stepped back and allowed Morgan and Jake to walk inside.

The circular chamber had a stark beauty. Twelve stone pillars supported high ceilings, with arches embracing tall windows around the perimeter of the circular room. Early morning light streaming in illuminated a stark black mosaic in the middle of the floor.

Morgan recognized it as the symbol Martin had showed her. The Black Sun, the Schwarze Sonne, a version of a pagan sun wheel used across many cultures, adopted as a rallying symbol for the Nazis and those who even now subscribed to their values.

As ever, with symbology, context was critical, and in this case, the Black Sun was enormous. Twelve lightning sig runes, like those used as the emblem of the SS, radiated out from a circular black heart. It seemed to suck the light out of the air, channeling it deep into the heart of the castle.

Klaus stood to one side next to a pillar and Morgan noticed he would not step onto the lines of the mosaic. In fact, he seemed to bristle as Jake walked over it. A curator's concern for the museum, or something else?

"Can you tell me more about the symbolism in the castle?" Morgan asked.

Klaus put his hands behind his back, clasping them as he paced up and down, clearly used to such questions.

"As Reichsführer, Himmler wanted to underpin the mission of the SS with elements that resonated with historical, mythical, and occult components. He chose this site as it is close to the possible location of the Irminsul, a legendary pillar sacred to early Germanic people, and important to the völkisch — or ultra-nationalist — enthusiasts within the SS. It's also near the fabled site of a battle in which Germanic tribes overthrew the Roman Empire, and Himmler believed it might be the site of an apocalyptic future conflict."

He nodded down at the Black Sun mosaic. "There were twelve Knights of the Teutonic Order, an ancient military order who defended true believers on the road to Jerusalem, and there were twelve senior SS officers who gathered here for strategic meetings. The castle also includes motifs from Grail legends and Germanic folklore, with rooms named after Arthurian and Teutonic heroes."

Klaus looked at his watch. "We don't have long until opening. Please have a quick look around and then I'll show you to the crypt."

He abruptly turned, walked over to one of the windows, and gazed outside, leaning against the wall with one hand. He tapped his index finger impatiently on the stone.

Morgan remained puzzled by the curator, but perhaps working in such a place for so long took its toll.

"Look at this," Jake called from one end of the chamber.

Morgan joined him in front of a framed architectural drawing hanging on the wall.

"This is Himmler's plan for the final SS complex. You can't get much more obvious than this." He indicated the lines on the map, which created the shape of a spearhead with the pointed tip formed by the triangular lines of Wewelsburg castle.

Morgan sighed. "Incredible. Even the architecture of this place underpins Himmler's obsession with the Spear."

Klaus turned from the window, walking swiftly over to join them, his eyes suddenly bright with interest. "Yes, indeed. Wewelsburg castle was to be the center of the Reich's new world after the eventual victory, with the Spear of Destiny and perhaps even the Grail at its heart."

Jake frowned. "But this was Himmler's castle, not Hitler's. Was there a power conflict between the two?"

Klaus paused, tilting his head to one side as he considered the question.

"Their views about the mystical certainly differed. Hitler

became focused on the practicalities of war, while Himmler never faltered from his pursuit of more esoteric truth. One of Hitler's last acts was to strip the Reichsführer of all his offices and order his arrest. So yes, there was conflict, but isn't there always in the machinations of war?"

Klaus pointedly looked at his watch. "Now, we must go. I'll show you the crypt, which I think is the reason for your visit."

Morgan and Jake followed Klaus down a flight of winding stairs and emerged into another circular stone room, this time with a domed ceiling decorated with a carved swastika. It was smaller than the ceremonial hall above, and more darkly intimate. Angled windows high up cast a dim light, illuminating a sunken circular pit contained by a low wall in the center of the crypt. A dipped recess in the middle was covered by a thin layer of gravel.

"This vault is modeled after Mycenaean domed tombs, carved into the foundations of the castle by Himmler's workers."

As Klaus spoke, Morgan couldn't help but think of the condemned prisoners whose lives paid for this place. As she looked around, she realized the vault must lie directly below the Black Sun mosaic above.

Klaus pointed at a piece of metal jutting up out of the central recess. "That is a gas pipe for the fire bowl with an eternal flame that would have burned here during the ceremonies."

"What ceremonies?" Jake asked.

Klaus shrugged. "No one knows. Now I have to get back up to the museum to open up for the day. You're welcome to stay and have a look around, although as you can see, there is little of interest down here. There's more information about Himmler and the SS on the placards in the public areas on your way out."

Without waiting for a reply, Klaus spun and hurried from the chamber, leaving them alone.

Jake stood with his back against one wall of the crypt. "Can you imagine what it must have been like down here back then? Himmler's SS men were the elite of their age, drawn from the upper echelons of society, able to trace their Aryan bloodline back for generations. They must have stood here in their formal black uniforms, wearing their death's head rings, and together, they began to... well, they must have done something. What do you think?"

Morgan shrugged. "Martin's research notes included some conspiracy theories, as well as proven history. Some say the Nazis summoned demons here and constrained them with this specially designed architecture, channelling them into the real world through possession of the living. Some say spirits of dead SS officers were summoned back, tethered to their death's head rings which were kept in a chest. Apparently, over ten thousand rings are still missing."

"Sounds like they got busy down here. Shame they still had the time to cause such destruction above. But it seems a pretty basic chamber for somewhere with such a reputation. There must be something else here."

As Jake walked more slowly around the crypt, studying the walls in more detail, Morgan stepped down to examine the dipped recess in the center of the crypt. There was something about the precision of the stacked chambers that made her curious.

Sacred numbers fascinated Himmler, and three was the most sacred in many traditions. If the Hall of the Supreme Leaders was a public room, and this chamber was for the special few, perhaps there was a third place, somewhere even more sacred, somewhere only Himmler and his closest men might go.

She knelt in the gravel and began to brush some of it aside. "Martin's notes indicated that Karl Maria Wiligut, an Austrian occultist and one of Himmler's personal staff within the SS, worked on the architectural plans for the castle. He also designed the Totenkopfring, the death's head ring, presented to SS officers after three years' service and returned to the castle after their deaths. Would Wiligut really have missed an opportunity to increase the occult powers of this place?"

She brushed away more of the loose gravel to reveal a ring of stark runes carved into the base of the recess around the gas nozzle, but there was something off about them. Morgan ran her fingertips over the asymmetrical indentations.

Jake hunkered down on the edge of the low wall next to her, then pulled a powerful torch from his bag. He shone it over the ground, helping to illuminate the shadowed area.

Morgan leaned down to look more closely at the gas nozzle in the center.

She nudged it.

It moved slightly, lifting several of the runes around it. Jake jumped down to join her and together, they tugged at the nozzle.

A cracking sound echoed in the crypt.

An outline of a small round trapdoor emerged amongst the indentations.

Jake gave the nozzle another yank, and the trapdoor eased open a little. Morgan reached under the door and pulled it up, revealing a metal ladder disappearing into darkness below. It looked like an access tunnel, perhaps to service the gas pipe.

But then dank air wafted up from below.

Morgan reared back from the stench as Jake coughed and spluttered in disgust. "What is that?"

Morgan covered her face with her arm and leaned over to look down into the tunnel, inhaling just a little more to try to discern what might be down there.

It was thick and cloying, with the earthy scent of ancient stone mingled with the sharp, iron tang of dried blood and the stink of voided bowels. It was the smell of fear, of torture, and of suffering. Something — or someone — had died down there far more recently than the Second World War.

Morgan looked over at Jake, and he grinned at her unspoken plan. He shone his torch down the shaft. "Ladies first."

Morgan clambered onto the ladder, her breath shallow as she tried not to inhale the reek of death.

She began to descend.

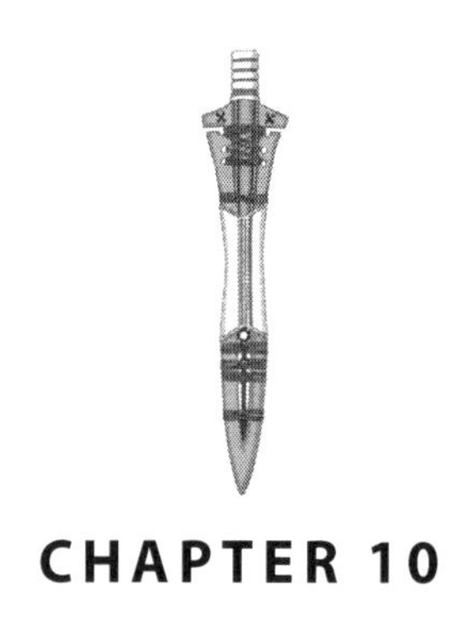

CHAPTER 10

THE SHAFT WAS NARROW, hewn from the rock upon which the castle stood. Its walls were rough and unyielding, and Morgan felt a rising unease as she climbed down into darkness, the stench clouding around her.

Thankfully, it was only a few meters before the passage opened out once more into a dark chamber. Morgan stepped off the ladder into the chamber and Jake soon emerged behind her, shining his more powerful torch around the room.

While the circular chamber echoed the shape of the two above, this was clearly the dark heart of the castle. The stone was almost black down here, both from its natural hue and, Morgan guessed, a sooty residue from candles and a sacred fire. The rock walls were carved with stark angular runes and occult symbols, and in the center of the circular chamber stood a black granite altar. Large enough to hold a man or a sizeable animal, it was pitted with knife marks and stained with dried blood. A death's head skull leered up from its surface, carved into the stone.

This chamber was no historical curiosity. It was clearly still used for some kind of sacrifice.

Morgan gazed up, picturing the sacred flame and the swastika in the chamber above, and beyond them, the black sun mosaic in the Hall of the Supreme Leaders. It was a triple layer of symbolism intended to lock in occult power.

She imagined the stone vault echoing with the chants of powerful men as they gathered in the dead of night, attempting to summon a dark power that would bestow victory upon the Reich in return for the sacrifice of so many. The legend of the Spear suggested that whoever claimed it could summon a good or an evil spirit and use its dominion for military might. What evil might the SS have summoned here?

"There's an inscription on the side of the altar." Jake used a translation app on his phone to scan the German words. "He who does not carry demonic seeds within him will never give birth to a new world." He raised an eyebrow. "I guess it's clear what they were trying to do down here."

"That line rings a bell from Martin's research." Morgan scrolled through her phone to the notes. "Here we are. That quote was underlined by Hitler in a book on magic by Ernst Schertel, a German mystic. The book was one of the most heavily annotated in Hitler's personal library, and it's now in the rare book collection in the Library of Congress in Washington, DC."

Jake circled the altar. "Do you think they managed to summon something here?"

"It's possible, at least based on our previous missions." Morgan thought of the demon in the crypt of bone, the infernal creatures that boiled out of the gates of hell, and how she had come too close to whatever diabolical power fueled the Black Anchorite. She and Jake had brushed up against many faces of evil, and Morgan sensed the jagged edge of it here.

"The Nazi ambition was to rule Europe for a thousand year Reich, so nothing would surprise me about how they intended to make that happen. Many of the elite were high on drugs, including a kind of crystal meth. Can you imagine the hallucinations that might have been conjured down here in the smoke and blood?"

She bent down to the corner of the altar to examine something hanging from the side. It was a leather cuff, tethered to the altar with a metal chain embedded in the stone.

"Those bastards," she murmured, imagining the terror of a victim tethered down here in the dark, surrounded by drugged-up SS officers calling on a dark power to emerge from the abyss.

Jake checked the other corners, discovering more of the cuffs. "They definitely shackled people here, but for what? Sacrifice, or some kind of ritual?"

Morgan took a deep breath. "Whatever it was back then, it's not over. This has been used recently. We need to find any other evidence, because once we're back up in the castle, we're calling the *Polizei* to shut this place down."

Jake shone his torch around the edges of the room. "There's something over there."

A heavy burgundy curtain hung across one wall, camouflaged by shadow.

Morgan tugged it aside to reveal a cramped anteroom with two old metal filing cabinets, their surfaces dull with age.

"These could definitely be from the war era." She opened one drawer. It slid out easily, clearly well-oiled and still in use.

Rows of personnel records lay inside, meticulously filed by date, stretching back to the early 1930s. There were passport-sized photos attached at the corners of each file, and some were bound with twine in bundles of varying sizes.

Morgan pulled one stack out to examine it more closely.

The top record and photo belonged to a senior member of the SS, and the first page traced his lineage back generations, underscoring the Nazi emphasis on blood purity.

Underneath, there were separate pages for different

young women, their expressions caught in wide-eyed terror in the photographs. Each had a date — or multiple dates — marked with runic symbols, echoing those carved around the crypt. Subsequent pages noted any children born, with photos ranging from toddlers to teenagers as each was followed through life. Some records had been updated to the present day, several generations later, with grandchildren and great-grandchildren.

Morgan wondered if this place was associated with the Lebensborn program, created by Himmler and designed to propagate Aryan lineage through offspring born to those with pure blood. SS and Wehrmacht officers, and others considered Aryan enough, were encouraged to mate with racially pure and healthy women, even those unmarried, in order to produce more children for the Reich.

She glanced back at the altar, horrified by what must have happened here. Men's violent control over women's bodily autonomy certainly wasn't a relic of the past, but this place was a different kind of evil. Her heart ached for those violated here.

"We need to photograph it all, or I'm afraid it will disappear into some kind of bureaucratic hole, or worse, be suppressed somehow."

She began snapping pictures with her phone, and Jake started on the second filing cabinet. They turned the pages quickly, capturing images of victims and perpetrators alike, as the decades passed through the records, evidence that this wretched place remained in use.

As Morgan flipped through one of the bundles, she stopped suddenly, recognizing something in the eyes and the jawline of a teenage boy, three generations on from a ritual performed back in Nazi times. What was it about him?

She turned another page to find a modern photo, a candid shot of the man training at a military camp, caught in profile, the tattoo on his neck clearly visible.

The soldier from Vienna.

Jake turned at her sharp inhalation of breath. "What is it?"

"The man I fought in the library. He's in this file. Check to see if you recognize any of the others."

As Jake turned back to his stack, Morgan scanned the record of the soldier. His name was Gabriel Blackthorn, and he was the grandson of a woman chained on this altar. A child originally born of rape in an occult ceremony that summoned a demon into the body of an SS officer, when human and the twisted unholy fused into one.

The quotation on the side of the altar made sense now. The Nazis were attempting to use demonic seeds to give birth to a new world, in a long game that went far beyond the immediacy of war in Europe.

Morgan considered Gabriel's strength while fighting, the instinct she had that he was holding something back, and his perception of her cursed blood. Was it possible that the ceremony had worked? And if so, how many more people like Gabriel were out there?

She read on. The documents noted the birth father was the son of a decorated SS officer. Gabriel had been adopted into a Christian family in the USA as a baby and followed through his childhood, during which he showed signs of excellence in many areas. He had been fast-tracked through army positions, and now led an elite military unit, Jericho Command.

Morgan snapped more photos as she wondered how much Gabriel knew of his dark ancestry.

A heavy clang suddenly resounded in the chamber, then the sound of metal grating on stone.

Jake spun around. "The trapdoor!"

He raced back into the crypt and scaled the short tunnel above. The sound of him battering the metal echoed down into the chamber, but he reappeared a minute later with a grim expression. "Someone shut us down here. We're trapped."

"The curator?"

"Either him or someone else who doesn't want this chamber found."

Jake frowned, tilted his head to one side, and held up a hand for quiet. In the silence, Morgan heard it, too.

The hiss of gas.

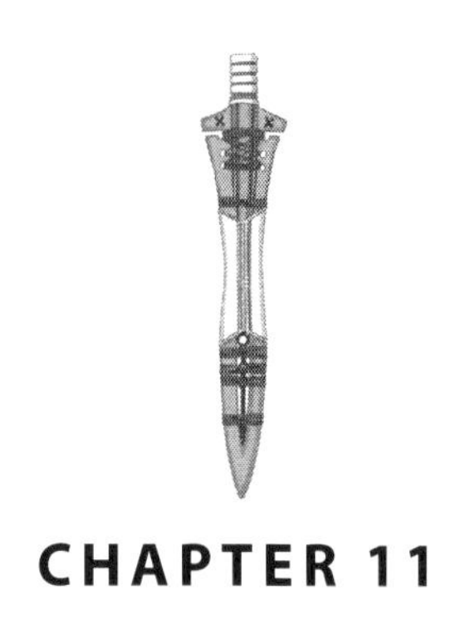

CHAPTER 11

THE SOUND WAS TERRIFYING given how many people the Nazis had murdered in gas chambers during the war. It was an efficient way to despatch vast numbers of people — historical evidence suggested that six thousand people per day were gassed with Zyklon B at Auschwitz alone.

"I refuse to die in a Nazi ritual crypt. We have to get out of here." Morgan channeled her anger into frantically searching the chamber.

She and Jake circled in opposite directions, feeling along the walls for any hidden seams or other ways out. Jake even checked below the altar, but there was nothing.

The continuous hissing was a sinister whisper, an invisible countdown to oblivion.

They crouched lower near to the floor, assuming the gas was likely some kind of hydrogen cyanide, a lighter-than-air gas like that used by the Nazis.

Morgan's breathing was shallow now, and she felt lightheaded, but she refused to give in to despair.

"There's no way the most senior Nazi officers would have entered the chamber down that tunnel, especially if there was a flame burning above in the fire pit. There has to be another doorway…" She spun around. "The storeroom."

She and Jake dashed back in; together they yanked the filing cabinets away from the back wall.

A narrow tunnel doglegged into darkness.

Jake shone his torch inside. "What do you think? The exit might be blocked at the other end. By then, it will be too late to come back this way."

Morgan coughed as the noxious fumes seeped into the storeroom. "No choice. We have to try it."

Jake met her gaze and reached out to squeeze her hand gently.

For a moment, she thought he was going to speak aloud the feelings they both held for each other. But then he smiled, let her hand go, and stooped to enter the low-ceilinged tunnel, his torch lighting the way.

Morgan followed him quickly, and they half crouched, half stumbled through the rocky passage, trying not to breathe too deeply.

The tunnel was narrow and the walls cold, seeming to press ever closer. They staggered on through twists and turns for a few minutes as Morgan leaned against the wall for support, every footstep like dragging through sand.

"We must be outside the castle walls now," Jake called back. "The air seems fresher too."

Morgan heard the hope in his voice and clung to it as darkness threatened to pull her under. The ghosts of women abused in that chamber seemed to follow her through the tunnel, chill fingers reaching out, entreating her to revenge them.

"There's another trapdoor," Jake shouted from up ahead.

A thud. A crack of metal.

A shaft of daylight pierced the gloom.

Jake clambered out into a forest clearing a little way outside the castle walls and helped Morgan climb out after him.

They pushed the trapdoor closed to keep the poison gas inside and sat inhaling the fresh air in desperate relief.

The sound of birdsong was incongruous, after the darkness they had emerged from. It was a natural sound of hope, evidence that whatever malevolent deeds occurred here, the wheel of life continued to turn. But while Himmler and the Third Reich were gone, their ideas clearly lived on in modern times — and Morgan was determined to at least make sure it did not thrive here once more.

After she caught her breath, her mind clear again, she looked up at the castle walls. "We need to get back in there and find the curator. Even if he wasn't the one who tried to kill us, he has to know what's down there."

They hurried back to the castle gates, past the tourists who wandered around the museum displays and up to the administration section.

But the curator's office was empty.

Morgan touched the side of a cup of coffee on the desk. It was still warm. "He left in a hurry. Maybe there was an alarm or a camera on that external hatch. He knew when we escaped the gas chamber."

"He can't have got far." Jake pulled out his phone. "I'll tell Marietti what we found. He can call in some favors at the Polizei to get them over here as fast as possible and set up roadblocks to catch Klaus."

As Jake stepped outside to make the call, Morgan searched the office.

A rack of shelving for merchandise sold in the museum shop dominated the space. Books about the castle and its history, tea towels, fridge magnets, and even colorful cuddly toys.

She rifled through the papers on the curator's desk, then pulled open a cupboard full of administration records. The inside of the cupboard looked too shallow for the size of the room.

Morgan frowned and knocked on the wooden back.

It rang hollow.

She pulled out the files and dumped them on the floor,

then ran her fingers around the back of the cupboard. She found a latch and removed a panel, revealing a Nazi swastika flag wrapped around something hard.

Morgan carefully lifted the parcel out and laid it on the desk, then unfolded the edges of the flag to reveal what lay within.

A blunted iron cross-guard from an ancient Roman lance, with a piece of copper wire wrapped around one end.

Jake came back into the room. "The police are on their way, and Marietti's cleared us. We don't need to stay for the investigation." He walked over. "Is that what I think it is?"

Morgan nodded. "It has to be. It makes sense that Himmler kept a piece of the real Spear here for ceremonies, even if the other fragments were hidden elsewhere. The copper wire matches the piece from the Hofburg."

The sound of sirens came from far off.

"I don't think we should leave this for the police." Morgan hesitated for a moment and then removed the fragment of the Spear from the Nazi flag.

She couldn't bear the thought of carrying such a repugnant piece of history, and besides, it was evidence that the curator was breaking the law in addition to what lay in the levels below the castle.

She grabbed a tea towel from the merchandise rack and wrapped the fragment of the Spear tightly, stuffing it into her backpack, before she and Jake hurried out of the castle.

As they sped back to the airport, Morgan emailed Martin images of what they'd found, including Gabriel's records, to add another piece to the puzzle.

Police cars with sirens blaring raced past in the other direction and there were roadblocks being set up already. While Morgan was confident the authorities would find Klaus and shut down the unhallowed chamber, she didn't have time to wait for their full investigation.

As they reached the airport, Martin messaged back with

an update on Gemma. She was in a critical condition, and he was still searching for a way to combine both medical and supernatural elements in a cure.

But he had a new direction for their search, based on the missions of Himmler's Ahnenerbe.

As she read the notes, Morgan frowned and looked over at Jake. "You're not going to be happy about our next destination."

* * *

A few hours later, General Ezekiel Stronghold sat in his office at Jericho Command, his brow furrowed in concentration as he reviewed the latest intelligence reports from his various teams currently on mission in different theaters of war throughout the world.

As he scrolled through the encrypted files, his phone vibrated with an incoming message. He glanced at the screen, his heart rate quickening as he read the terse words from an asset embedded with the German police, someone who hid their allegiance but still upheld the values of the SS.

There was only one word — Wewelsburg — and an attached video from a security camera.

Ezekiel's mouth went dry.

The chamber beneath the SS crypt was never meant to be discovered, its dark history kept secret along with the demonic seeds planted in its depths. The Spear fragment remained there to continue the rituals of the past, and he had intended to retrieve it before the endgame. But now, if it fell into the wrong hands, it could unravel decades of careful planning.

With a muttered curse, Ezekiel opened the security video.

The camera showed the curator's empty office, with papers scattered across the floor and a cupboard door hanging open.

He rewound the footage, his pulse pounding in his ears. Two figures moved into view — a man and a woman. He didn't recognize them, but their purposeful movements and the way they systematically searched the office spoke of military training.

Ezekiel watched as the woman pulled something from the back of the cupboard — a Nazi flag wrapped around an object. His breath caught in his throat as she carefully unfolded the red fabric to reveal the iron cross-guard, a piece of the Spear bound in copper wire.

He hadn't seen it since the last time he took part in the ritual more than a decade ago, but its dark aura seemed to burn through the screen. It was powerful then, and would be even more powerful when joined with the other pieces.

On screen, the woman wrapped the Spear fragment in another cloth and stuffed it into her backpack before hurrying out of the office with her companion.

Ezekiel slammed his phone down, his mind racing. He had to act fast. He needed to retrieve that piece from those who stole it.

Another text arrived from his police asset with a flight plan filed from the airport near Wewelsburg.

Ezekiel called another number on his phone. It rang once, twice before a voice answered, cold and clipped.

"Blackthorn."

"Mobilize your team, Gabriel." Ezekiel kept his voice steady, belying the urgency thrumming through his veins. "Wheels up in an hour. I'll send through the details."

"Understood."

As he ended the call, Ezekiel leaned back in his chair, his fingers finding the death's head ring under his shirt. His family had sacrificed so much, and he had personally sacrificed even more to walk a path steeped in shadow and blood, all in service to a higher purpose.

The demonic seeds planted long ago were finally bearing fruit. He would see this harvest through, no matter the cost.

CHAPTER 12

MORGAN FOLLOWED JAKE OUT of the plane into Xining Caojiapu International Airport in China. She was a little weary from the nine-hour flight from Germany, but had managed some sleep and spent the rest of the time reading Martin's extensive documents on the Nazi expedition to Tibet back in 1938.

Flying directly to Tibet would be faster but would also put them at risk for debilitating altitude sickness, and Jake was susceptible, so they had to proceed carefully. The slower train from Xining, along the Qinghai–Tibet Railway, provided gradual adjustment, allowing acclimatization to the altitude, and was also renowned for its stunning mountainous landscape.

ARKANE Director Marietti had arranged short-term academic visas to travel through China to Lhasa, the capital of the Tibet Autonomous Region of China. The status of the country and its people had been contested over generations, but Morgan knew they couldn't risk political opinion on this visit. The mission was to discover whether there was a piece of the Spear in Lhasa, and to do that, they had to get there first.

As they walked through the customs area, Jake leaned in, his voice barely above a whisper. "We're being watched."

"Of course we are. We're Westerners in China heading for a center of political unrest. But there's no reason for them to stop us."

Morgan thought of the piece of the Spear wrapped inside her luggage. It didn't look like anything significant, so it shouldn't be an issue, but her heart raced at the possibility of discovery.

They grabbed their bags and headed for the exit, but as they weaved their way through families and groups of tourists, three Chinese military guards headed in their direction. There was no point in trying to get away. Morgan stopped, with Jake beside her, as the guards approached.

"Extra security check needed. Come with us." The leader's tone was curt, his expression cold.

Morgan smiled. "Of course. Is there a problem?"

The man spun away without answering, and one of the other guards indicated they should follow.

As they were led from the bustling terminal and into the stark isolation of an interrogation room, Morgan evaluated their options. She knew Jake would be doing the same. But this was China, and Western organizations like ARKANE had little sway here. They needed to wait and see what this was about.

The room was a sterile box, the air stale, the lighting harsh and unforgiving. There was a metal table and a few hard chairs. The leader gestured to them and Morgan sat down, Jake next to her.

She breathed slowly, holding back all the words she wanted to say. There was no point in provoking a confrontation as much as every fibre of her being screamed to get out of here.

Two of the guards unpacked their bags while the leader watched, his face impassive. It didn't take long until their stuff was laid out. The metal piece of the Spear was among the items, but the guards paid it no special attention.

"Why are you here?" the leader asked.

"We're academics," Morgan said softly, keeping her tone respectful. "We want to take the train across your beautiful country and look at some books in the library of the Potala Palace in Lhasa."

She pointed at the pages of meticulous documentation Martin had procured, including letters from a prestigious British university, a detailed itinerary, and academic credentials. "You can see our research proposal there and permissions granted by the appropriate officials."

The leader scrutinized the documents page by page, his lips pressed tightly together, his brow furrowed as he read.

The minutes passed.

Morgan tried to relax, not daring to show any sign of concern. She trusted Martin, but any deviation from what was expected in terms of documentation would be an issue. Detention in a Chinese prison was not something she wished to experience, and she knew Jake would fight back if things escalated.

Eventually, the leader put the papers back on the table. "This seems in order, but any deviation from your itinerary will be investigated. I'll notify the military in Lhasa of your impending arrival."

The extra scrutiny was a setback, as they were absolutely intending to go off the itinerary, but they'd face that possibility when it arrived.

The leader gestured at their gear. "Repack now. You will be escorted to the train to make sure you leave on time."

Or to make sure they actually boarded and left the area. Morgan didn't say the words aloud, but that was clearly the implication.

"Thanks for your help," Jake said with a smile. The leader narrowed his eyes, his mouth twitching as he tried to decide whether Jake was being disrespectful.

After a moment, he spun and walked out of the room,

leaving the two others to watch as Morgan and Jake repacked their gear.

They would have to be careful in the days ahead. One step out of line and they would be at the mercy of the Chinese military.

The guards escorted them to the entrance of the Qinghai–Tibet Railway station, where they once more presented their papers and the medical card required to board. Each carriage had an extra oxygen supply and there were doctors on the train, but a health form was required for the high-elevation travel to prevent those at serious risk from attempting the trip.

They boarded and found their place in a private modern cabin with comfortable seats that reclined in front of a huge picture window, designed to highlight the spectacular scenery as the train sped along. There was a snack cupboard and a small fridge full of bottled water.

Morgan had never suffered altitude sickness, but Jake had struggled in the past on missions before she had joined ARKANE. Symptoms included headaches and nausea, confusion and balance issues, coughing and being short of breath. In extreme cases, fluid in the lungs and brain could cause death. It wasn't something to be taken lightly and affected even the fittest of people.

They had both taken medication to help with the adjustment, and now Jake reclined in his seat, a bottle of water in his hand to help with hydration, his eyes closed to get some rest.

Ascending slowly was the best way to acclimatize, but Morgan was acutely aware of how the altitude might impair Jake. There were so many unknowns on this mission. His physical state was just another variable, but for now, all she could do was gaze out the window as the train left the station.

The urban sprawl receded as the tracks crossed an open

plain where yaks grazed slowly in verdant meadows, their shaggy coats a deep, rich brown against the vibrant green of the grass. The animals moved slowly, methodically, as if in tune with the timeless rhythm of the land. In adjacent fields, farmers toiled, their backs bent as they worked the fertile soil. They moved with practiced grace, their hands deftly tending to the crops that sustained them and their families. It was not a life that Morgan wanted, but the simplicity of the pastoral scene gave her a moment of peace.

In the distance, the mountains rose up, their peaks dusted with eternal snow, the valleys between them carved by ancient glaciers. Streams and rivers snaked their way down, their waters crystal clear and icy cold, fed by the melting snow from the peaks above. The train headed on and up; soon they were in the heart of the mountains, surrounded by towering peaks, each carriage a speck against the immense landscape.

As Morgan stared out at the stark beauty, she remembered what she'd read in Martin's dossier about the Nazi expedition.

The group had traveled north through British India, gaining permissions to travel through Sikkim before the outbreak of war. The train route didn't exist in 1938, so the journey took months rather than hours. They crossed the snowy passes and rugged mountains with a team of porters and animals to carry their gear, traveling under the guise of an anthropological and scientific delegation. In reality, they were searching for the supernatural origin of the Aryan race on Himmler's orders, perhaps intending to channel more power into the fragment of the Spear they carried. But had they found what they were looking for out here in the Himalayas?

Jake's voice cut through her thoughts. "Makes our lives seem small in the grand scheme of things, doesn't it?"

She turned. "I didn't know you were awake. How are you feeling?"

"Like a weak human with a physical body that is failing fast." He grimaced. "I'm struggling, to be honest. How about you?"

"I'm good, but you know this isn't under your control, right? You can't will yourself to overcome it."

"I know, but that doesn't make it any easier."

Morgan reached up and unhooked a nasal cannula from the oxygen unit behind Jake's seat. "Here, put this on. It will help."

He sighed as he reluctantly attached it to his nostrils. "I hate being an invalid."

"Oh, shut up and rest. Let me enjoy the view."

Morgan turned back to the mountains as they reached another pass, crossing a bridge over a rocky chasm that plummeted to the depths of the earth.

The scale was immense, and Morgan felt a sense of being out of time. A realization that she was nothing on the face of the earth, a mere flicker of light against the backdrop of history.

It was a comfort of sorts to know that the world would go on regardless of what happened in her generation. Yet she could not just sit and meditate on a mountaintop. Every breath she took was another that Gemma struggled for back in Oxford, and if the Spear had some possibility of healing power, she would do everything to find the other pieces.

A signal station ahead seemed the size of a toy against the backdrop of the colossal mountains, and Morgan noticed the peaks were now hidden in dense, dark clouds. They were heading into a storm.

She checked her watch. They couldn't be that far from Lhasa now, but it looked like they'd reach it in terrible weather.

As the train raced across the terrain, it began to hail, the clatter of the stones against the windows muted by the noise of the train on the tracks.

Morgan turned to look at Jake, noting the lines around his mouth, his clenched fists. He wouldn't admit to the pain, but he was clearly feeling it. Life was fragile here in the mountains and there were so many ways to die.

A sudden explosion came from the front of the train.

The brakes squealed.

The wheels scraped on the tracks.

The train lurched violently, as a monstrous groan of metal on metal echoed through the carriage.

Morgan grabbed Jake's arm, steadying him as the lights flickered.

Screams filled the air from the other carriages as the train ground to a halt.

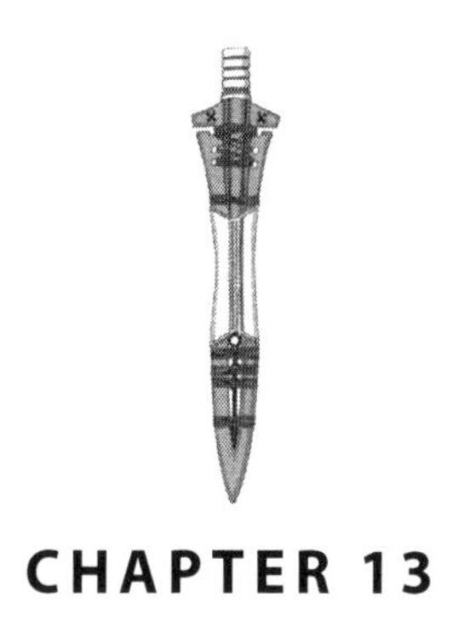

CHAPTER 13

"What the hell was that?" Jake gasped, pulling the cannula from his nostrils. "Some kind of accident?"

Morgan pressed her face against the window, trying to see what was happening.

In the hailstorm, she could just make out a team of commandos in white military gear heading to the front of the train, guns held out as they advanced in attack formation.

"Looks like an ambush. Could be Tibetan separatists." But their gear was seriously professional, and the way the team moved made Morgan think of the soldiers who had come for them in Vienna.

Gunfire erupted from the carriages ahead as the Chinese soldiers aboard the train engaged the invaders.

"I'm going to see what's happening." Morgan slipped out of the cabin before Jake could protest.

She hurried toward the front of the train.

The corridor was chaos, with a surge of panicked tourists and shouts from the Chinese soldiers trying to maintain order.

She weaved around scared and screaming passengers until she could see active fighting in the carriage ahead. The Chinese military were holding their ground, but beyond them, she glimpsed one of the invaders.

He wore the colors of a Tibetan separatist group and a ski mask, but at the gap where it met his neck, Morgan saw a rune tattoo.

Gabriel Blackthorn.

Time slowed, and for a moment, she considered surrendering to him. Perhaps he would help her figure out the curse and save Gemma, and she would gladly trade her life to save her niece.

A soldier burst out of the carriage.

He shouted at Morgan in Chinese, clearly telling her to get back.

Gunfire rattled.

The soldier dropped to the ground, clutching his chest.

The blood on his uniform galvanized Morgan into action. She could not risk testing Gabriel's mercy, especially with Jake so sick. She turned and ran, darting back along the train.

"What's happening?" Jake asked as she burst back into the carriage.

"It's the soldiers from Vienna. We can't let them find us." She grabbed their bags. "There's an emergency carriage at the end of the train. We need to get back there."

Jake struggled to his feet, his face pale.

Morgan helped him up. "Can you make it?"

Jake nodded, his jaw clenched.

They pushed their way through the chaos of the train car, fighting against the tide of panicked passengers. The air was thick with the acrid scent of smoke and the metallic tang of blood, and the flickering emergency lights cast an eerie, pulsing glow over the scene.

Morgan pulled Jake forward as they clambered over fallen luggage and debris.

They passed a young woman clutching a wailing infant to her chest, her eyes wide with terror as she stumbled past. An elderly man lay slumped against the wall, his head lolling at an unnatural angle, moaning softly. Morgan wished she could stop and help, but they were running out of time.

As they neared the end of the carriage, a group of Chinese military personnel ran back the other way, their faces grim and determined as they pushed past. The soldiers were heavily armed, their weapons glinting in the flickering light, and their shouts echoed through the confined space as they barked orders to the passengers to remain in place.

Morgan hoped the Chinese soldiers might keep the invaders busy long enough that she and Jake could make it to safety. She glanced out the window. The storm raged on, with howling wind and driving snow. Their options were running out.

With a final push, they broke through the crowd and stumbled into the last passenger car, their lungs burning with the effort. The passengers here cowered in their cabins, obeying the orders from the military now broadcasted over the train loudspeakers, so the corridor was empty.

Morgan tried the door to the emergency carriage, rattling the handle. It was locked.

They didn't have time for an elegant solution, so Morgan smashed the window and released the lock through the broken glass. The sound of the alarm dissipated in the general mayhem, and they hurried inside.

The compartment housed racks of supplies to be used if the train was trapped in a storm in the mountains, with survival shelters, warm clothing, and ration packs lined up in rows.

Jake sagged down to the floor, sitting with his back against the side of the carriage as Morgan scanned the shelves, assessing their options.

The storm was upon them now, and the windows rattled with the force of wind and hail. The outside world was a blizzard of white, and visibility was almost zero in the swirl of sleet.

"You need to go on." Jake's voice was tense and low. "Don't wait for me."

Morgan could hear his unspoken pain, but she wouldn't leave him. He had been in Vienna, too. The soldiers knew his face. He would be taken, and nothing was worth that.

"You're coming. No arguments. Can you stand?"

After a moment, he nodded, teeth clenched. "Help me into one of those thick jackets. I'm sorry, Morgan, but you'll need to carry the gear."

"Not a problem. I've been sitting around too much on this train. It's time for a workout."

She grabbed a big rucksack and stuffed their things in, along with the Spear fragment, followed by an emergency shelter, tightly packed sleeping bags, and ration packs.

The sound of gunshots came from the next carriage.

They were out of time.

Morgan pushed open the emergency door at the end of the train.

The wind howled in, slamming them back with its force, the chill making her gasp.

Morgan leaned into it, helping Jake out and on to the tracks. They hunkered low as they pushed their way out into the onslaught of the weather, the storm both a threat and their only chance of survival.

* * *

Gabriel Blackthorn surged through the train, his weapon at the ready, as his Jericho Command team engaged the Chinese soldiers in close combat.

They had to be quick. They couldn't risk capture. The mission was to retrieve the Spear fragment stolen from Wewelsburg and get out. General Stronghold had emphasized they take no prisoners, adding that death was preferable for those who had taken what was rightfully his. But

Gabriel wrestled with indecision. The woman from the Vienna library was here and he wanted a chance to talk to her. He needed to understand what it was about her cursed blood that called to the darkness within him.

Muzzle flashes strobed in the flickering lights, and screams of terrified passengers echoed off the walls.

"Three hostiles down in the next car," one of his men reported through the comms link. "No sign of the targets."

"Copy that." Failure was not an option, not with the general himself overseeing this mission. They had to secure the Spear fragment at any cost.

Gabriel kicked open the door to the next car, diving low as a barrage of gunfire raked the wall above him.

Rolling to his feet, he unleashed a volley of shots, dropping two Chinese soldiers before they could react.

"Chinese military incoming out of Lhasa. ETA fifteen minutes." The voice in the comms was from Central Oversight.

Gabriel cursed under his breath. They were almost out of time.

He pushed forward, his senses straining to pick up any trace of the woman beneath the cacophony of battle. The acrid scent of gunpowder mingled with the coppery tang of blood, and beneath it all, the faintest whisper of her scent lingered with an edge of jasmine and steel.

He followed it, his heart pounding in time with the gunshots and screams.

She was close, so close he could almost taste her on the air.

He shot two more soldiers as he tracked the scent, finally reaching a cabin where it was the strongest.

Gabriel burst inside, gun leveled.

But the carriage was empty.

No sign of the woman or her male companion. Only the howling blizzard outside.

"Abort! Abort!"

Central Oversight was insistent, and Gabriel knew it would be a close call to escape before the main military force arrived. They had no choice but to leave now.

He repeated the command to his team over comms and took one last glance around the carriage. She was close, but somehow she had escaped the train undetected.

The general would not be pleased at this setback, but no matter. There was only one place she could be heading next. Gabriel would regroup with his team and they would travel to Lhasa.

The Spear fragment would be his soon, and so would the mysterious woman.

* * *

Morgan urged Jake on through the snow. The storm would hide their tracks within a minute or two. They just had to get further away from the train and find somewhere to shelter before the soldiers even realized they had been there.

They hobbled on, sinking deeper with every footstep.

Morgan angled away from the train tracks, and within meters, they were standing in a swirl of white, unable to tell which direction the train was in.

She could only hope that the invading soldiers would need to retreat as fast as they had arrived. Whoever they were, they would avoid direct conflict with the Chinese military reinforcements that were sure to be there soon. They would have assumed a fast assault and a swift capture, followed by rapid withdrawal, avoiding engagement with a larger force.

No American soldier would risk capture in this part of the world. At least she hoped so, because if they fanned out into the snow, the soldiers would find her and Jake soon enough. They would die quickly by bullet or slowly in the storm, or be left for the Chinese military to deal with. The Spear fragment would be taken, and any hope for Gemma lost.

If they died out here, at least they might be part of the long tradition of Tibetan sky burial. Dead bodies were cut up into pieces and offered to vultures — part of the circle of life, evidence of the transience of existence. Flesh became food, and then as the vultures took flight, each atom might become one with the sky and the mountain winds. While there was poetry in that, they had a mission to complete.

Morgan pushed away the dark thoughts and half-dragged Jake on, squinting into the blizzard. The white flakes stung her eyes, prickling her skin and reducing the world to a swirl of ferocious sound.

The weight of the pack, along with Jake leaning against her, was almost too much to bear, but she struggled on.

The wind whipped around them, howling as if a demon enraged. Morgan suddenly stumbled as her foot sank into a snowdrift, then through it into ankle-deep water so cold it made her gasp.

She let go of Jake to steady herself and he took two more staggering steps ahead of her into the blizzard — plunging through a thin layer of ice into a glacial river.

CHAPTER 14

"JAKE!" MORGAN DROPPED THE pack by the bank and darted forward to try to reach him.

He gasped and spluttered in the fast-moving river, dragged down by his water-logged clothes.

Morgan stepped into the shallows and reached for his outstretched hand.

Their fingers brushed — but Jake was swept on, coughing and wheezing as he fought desperately to escape the current with heavy limbs.

Morgan sprinted ahead along the bank and waded out into the channel to intercept him. She clenched her chattering teeth against the chill of the water that seemed to pierce deep into her bones.

She reached for him.

This time, their fingers locked. Morgan hauled Jake back toward the bank until he could find purchase with his boots on the rocky shoreline.

They stumbled out onto the bank and lay panting together on the stony shore as snow fell and melted on the surrounding rocks. Jake's lips were blue, his skin too pale, his eyes closed.

He looked like a corpse.

Morgan immediately thrust the thought from her mind.

They would not die here after everything they had been through together.

She rolled over and wrapped her arms around Jake, pulling him close so the warmer skin of her face met his frigid cheek.

"I've got you. You're okay now."

But her words rang hollow. They both knew the cold would kill them faster now they were wet and exhausted.

Jake pressed his head close to hers as he shivered violently. "I'm so sorry, Morgan… I shouldn't have come. I can't be the partner you need… With this weakness."

Morgan hugged him closer, understanding how much he hated his frailty. She had felt the same many times, and in those dark moments, he had been her strength. "I can't do this without you. I need you, Jake, and I'm not leaving you here."

She looked out across the river. The other side was now clearly visible a few meters away. "It looks like the storm is losing its fury. I'll go back along the bank and get the pack. We'll shelter here and get some sleep."

Morgan pulled away from the embrace, aware that her clothes were freezing against her skin. They both had to get warm — and soon.

"I won't be long."

She jogged back along the riverbank.

They hadn't gone far, but hopefully still far enough from the train to avoid the inevitable post invasion investigation. As she ran, Morgan pushed down the painful prickling sensation in her limbs, the burning an early sign of frostbite. She had learned to compartmentalize, and right now, focusing on her discomfort served no purpose.

Within a few minutes, she found the discarded pack, hefted it on, and hurried back to Jake, careful where she put her feet on the slippery ground. She couldn't afford to injure herself right now.

The snow was falling more gently as Morgan rounded the final corner. Jake lay curled up on the stones — unmoving.

Her heart skipped a beat. Was she too late?

He shivered violently, and she breathed a sigh of relief, quickening her pace to reach him.

Morgan dropped the pack, crouched down, and whispered. "I'm here. Hang on just a few more minutes."

She swiftly erected the emergency shelter, nestling it snug against a snow bank so they couldn't be seen by anyone approaching.

It would be just big enough for them both to squeeze into. She helped Jake up and out of his wet clothes until he was only in boxer shorts. Morgan wrapped an emergency blanket around him and helped him crawl into the shelter. He huddled, trembling, while she stripped down to her underwear and scrambled inside.

Morgan zipped the door shut and pulled Jake close, opening her blanket so they were skin to skin. She gritted her teeth as the chill of his body sapped the warmth from hers and pushed her mind out into the white expanse beyond. She counted the seconds as she tightened her grip around him, willing him to live.

As the minutes passed, Jake's shivers finally slowed. His teeth stopped chattering. His breathing slowed and became easier. He laid his head on her shoulder, and Morgan felt his muscles relax as he fell asleep.

She listened to his rhythmic breathing as the storm ebbed outside, aware of how close their bodies were now the emergency had passed.

Morgan pressed her cheek into Jake's hair and stroked the skin of his shoulder, sensing the hard muscle beneath.

While there had always been chemistry between them, they had never crossed the line into being more than agent partners. There had been opportunities in the past and no doubt there would be again, but while they remained purely work colleagues and friends, their distance gave them a measure of safety.

They had both been broken by grief in the past and neither of them could bear to have someone so close again, especially in their line of work. But perhaps here in the storm's anonymity, they could hold each other and let it be nothing more than a human connection for warmth and safety.

Morgan adjusted her position so she could lean into Jake, the pair of them propped up, wrapped together inside the emergency blankets. She closed her eyes and let the darkness come.

* * *

A loud metallic hammering jerked Morgan back into consciousness.

"What was that?" Jake groaned.

He raised his head; he was bleary-eyed, but his lips were no longer blue. His skin was warm and—

Morgan pulled away, suddenly aware of how close their almost naked bodies were.

"I'll go outside and look."

She avoided his gaze and swiftly crawled outside the tent.

Her discarded clothes were stiff and freezing cold, but she exhaled hard and channeled the sensation into calming her beating heart as she put them on. In another life, she and Jake might have curled up together and made the most of being alone, but now he seemed to be recovering, they needed to get to Lhasa.

Martin Klein had arranged a meeting with a particular monk, someone he had met on a shared interest forum, and there was still a chance they could make the appointment.

The weak rays of early morning sun lit the river they

were camped beside. As the hammering continued, Morgan edged up the bank of snow sheltering the river from the main valley and peered toward the source of the noise.

The train lay stopped on the tracks a few kilometers across the valley and Morgan could just make out the faces of passengers peering out the windows. A group of Chinese engineers worked at the front, drilling and hammering to straighten out the section damaged in the attack.

It looked like it would take at least another hour to fix, and there didn't seem to be any other military around, but they couldn't just climb out of the bank and walk toward the train. It would look too suspicious.

Morgan traced the curve of the river, assessing its trajectory.

If they stayed low within its banks, they might be able to make their way toward the back of the emergency coach, remaining out of sight until the last minute.

It would be close, but if Jake was strong enough, they could make it back inside before the train headed along the last stretch into Lhasa. The military must have swept through the carriages in the explosion's aftermath, so if luck was on their side, they could re-enter the train and disembark with all the other passengers. No harm done.

If Jake was strong enough.

Morgan ducked back down below the edge of the bank and turned to the shelter.

Jake stood outside, almost naked, his muscular back muscles tensing as he stretched. He bent to cup some freezing river water and splashed his face, exhaling sharply as the cold hit his skin. Morgan bit her lip, but she didn't look away.

He turned around, met her gaze, and gave a wry smile, the corkscrew scar twisting up to his brow. "Thanks for keeping me warm. I think I'm all good now."

Morgan could only nod in agreement.

"What's happening up there?" Jake asked as he pulled on his rigid clothes.

Now he was fully dressed, Morgan could breathe more easily again. "They're fixing the tracks, so the train should move again soon. If we follow the bank, I think we might be able to get back inside and catch a lift for the last kilometers to Lhasa. But only if…"

"Only if I'm strong enough." Jake grinned. "Actually, I think the bath and some sleep finished off any symptoms. I'm ready to go — and this time, I'll carry the pack."

They quickly stuffed everything back inside and double-timed it along the bank of the river. They splashed through the shallow water at the edge, the sound drowned out by the hammering that only grew more intense as they neared the end of the train.

Morgan stopped several times to edge up the bank and check their position. Soon enough, they made it to a spot close to where they could make a run for the emergency carriage.

Shouts from the engineers suddenly echoed through the air.

The engine started up, and the train inched forward over the most damaged section of the track.

Morgan and Jake raced up the bank and sprinted toward the last carriage.

The train began to accelerate.

Jake pulled ahead. Even with the weight of the pack, his legs were longer, and he was faster over short distances. He jumped up onto the back of the train and turned, stretching out his hand to Morgan.

The look on his face was sheer exhilaration. She couldn't help smiling as she jumped, taking his hand as he pulled her up onto the platform and held her close.

"This is so much fun," he whispered. "But only because I'm with you."

He held her for just a beat longer than was necessary, their faces close to touching, their breath mingling.

The train jolted forward.

Morgan grabbed the emergency handle and pushed on the door. They tumbled inside.

A Chinese train steward counting the emergency packs on the shelf turned, his expression quizzical.

Jake didn't miss a beat. He put the pack on the floor and pulled out their personal gear along with the Spear fragment. He held out the pack to the steward as the used emergency blankets crinkled inside. "Thanks for the loan, but we're good to return to our cabin now."

The man looked confused, but he didn't follow as they walked past him and out the emergency carriage.

The train sped up, rattling along the tracks away from the valley.

Morgan was on high alert as they hurried down the corridor back toward their cabin. What if the Chinese military were waiting in their carriage? What if they were detained after everything they had risked in the snow?

But they opened the door of the cabin to find it just as they had left it.

Jake sank down into a chair and pulled open the snack cupboard. He tossed a chocolate bar to Morgan and ripped the wrapper off another, wolfing it down in two bites. Yes, he was definitely back on form.

As the train accelerated once more, Morgan could only hope they would find what they sought in Lhasa, as she had a feeling they hadn't seen the last of Gabriel Blackthorn.

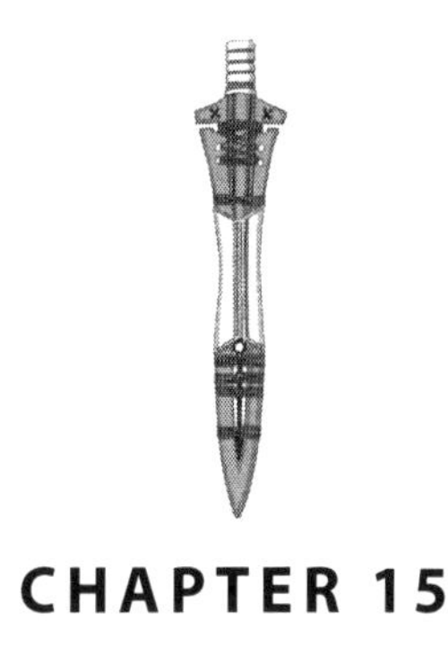

CHAPTER 15

THE TRAIN CRESTED THE final rise and Morgan gazed out at Lhasa as the morning sun cast a golden glow across the city. It was the 'place of gods' in the local language, the ancient capital of Tibet, and now the heart of the Tibet Autonomous Region in southwest China.

Buddhist prayer flags in vibrant colors fluttered in the wind by the side of the tracks, their silent blessings dancing away into the clear, crisp air as the train pulled into the station.

Chinese soldiers paced the platform, eyeing the train with suspicion as it made its last stop.

Morgan grabbed her bag. "Let's go. There should be a monk meeting us."

Jake raised an eyebrow. "If we make it out of the station through these soldiers." He picked up his pack. "Let's give it a try."

They stepped off the train onto the platform and walked slowly along with the crowd toward the military checkpoint.

Morgan's heart pounded as they reached the line of Chinese guards, but the soldier checked her papers quickly and waved her through, with Jake right behind.

They emerged into a busy transit station with the cacophony of noisy tourists and the clang of bells adding to the chaotic scene.

Morgan stood for a moment, scanning the crowd for the man they were supposed to meet. There were quite a few monks walking through the station, but as the crowd parted, she saw a particular one standing motionless by a pillar.

The young monk looked around twenty years old and exuded a sense of calm that seemed to create space around him, even in the bustling hall. He had a shaven head and wore traditional maroon and saffron robes draped around his slender body. He held simple wooden mala beads, his fingers counting off the prayers he was surely reciting in his mind.

He met Morgan's gaze across the busy hallway and smiled in welcome. She couldn't help but smile back. He beckoned and stood waiting while Morgan and Jake weaved their way through the crowds.

"*Tashi delek*. I'm Tenzin, a friend of Martin Klein. Welcome to Lhasa." He held his hands over his heart in a prayer pose and bowed slightly.

Morgan returned the greeting. "Thank you for meeting us."

Jake bowed along with her. "It's been quite the journey."

Tenzin frowned. "Yes, I heard the train had been hijacked. I was worried, so it's good to see you, especially as your library visit is scheduled for the next hour. I thought we'd have more time, but now we must hurry. The monks are very particular." He glanced to one side at the Chinese military. "And there are others whose attention we do not want to attract by deviating from your itinerary."

Tenzin led them outside and flagged down a taxi. They clambered in and traveled the last few kilometers across the Lhasa River and along its banks, before emerging in a square in front of the Potala Palace.

"It's stunning." Morgan gazed up at the majestic structure painted in shades of deep maroon and gold, perched on the Red Hill in the center of the city. White steps zigzagged up toward the palace, while hundreds of windows gazed out across the mountainous region.

Tenzin smiled. "I'm glad you like it. The Potala Palace was once the winter residence of the Dalai Lamas. It's now a museum with thirteen stories of buildings, over a thousand rooms, and more than ten thousand shrines."

Morgan knew better than to ask what Tenzin felt about the political situation. The fact he was willing to help them said enough. Martin had met Tenzin on a white hat hacker forum, and Morgan found it incongruous to imagine the monk exploring freely in cyberspace while being so constrained in his physical life.

The palace was a UNESCO World Heritage Site, and the Chinese continued to spend millions on preserving its cultural history. Intricate murals and sacred relics whispered stories of a bygone era, and its fabled library, founded in the seventh century, had over eighty thousand ancient manuscripts, with only five percent of them translated. This place was a maze of knowledge they could easily become lost in, and Morgan could only hope that Tenzin might help them find what they were looking for.

He pointed to the stairs. "Now, we climb. But we'll go slowly as I know it's hard going for foreigners unused to our altitude."

Jake grinned at Morgan. "Oh, I'm fine, raring to go."

She rolled her eyes and handed him her bag. "You can carry this, then."

They began to ascend the hundreds of steps up to the palace and soon they were silent except for their labored breathing. Tenzin seemed to float up with effortless grace, but he didn't hurry them, waiting on each of the terraces as Morgan and Jake stopped to catch their breath.

On one landing, Morgan gazed out at the city below, as the scent of juniper incense wafted up on a chill breeze. The distant sound of chanting monks and pilgrims mingled with the tinkle of bells and the low hum of the bustling marketplace below.

Tenzin explained the slow pace of the pilgrims, who halted often on the ascent. "With each step, we reflect on the teachings of the Buddha, on the impermanence of life, and on the interconnectedness of all beings. The climb is deliberately arduous. It's a test of endurance, patience, and the will to continue. A reminder of the effort required to overcome the obstacles of ignorance and desire that bind us to the cycle of suffering."

They continued to ascend and soon reached a terrace that led into the main palace.

Bypassing the grand entrance, Tenzin led them through an unassuming side door. "We will avoid most of the tourists and the guards this way."

"Do you work here?" Morgan asked.

Tenzin nodded. "I'm part of the library preservation project. The Chinese government is spending millions on it over the next decade to preserve the ancient manuscripts and books we have here. That's how I met your friend, Martin. I was searching for a way we might speed up the translations. The manuscripts are mostly written in a highly specialized language, and they're fragile. We need to scan them and use artificial intelligence tools to help us. Martin worked on a similar project at the Vatican, I believe."

"Was he able to help you?" Morgan asked, wondering whether the combination of ancient faith and modern technology might reveal new secrets in the years to come.

Tenzin nodded with enthusiasm. "Yes, and we still correspond over new techniques. But of course, we can only translate the texts we can scan, and many of the oldest works are written on thin paper or even brittle tree bark. We need more powerful scanning technology and more nuanced imaging, which is why I am most encouraged by the Vesuvius Challenge. It demonstrated that we might unlock the secrets of even the most ancient scrolls here."

He turned into a corridor dimly lit by the soft, flickering glow of butter lamps, their warm light casting dancing shadows on the stone walls. The lamps were placed at regular intervals along the corridor, each one a small, brass vessel carved with sacred symbols, and filled with yak butter and a single, flickering wick. The flames danced and swayed in the gentle draft that whispered through the palace, wafting the scent of the burning butter through the air.

"What's the Vesuvius Challenge?" Jake asked.

Tenzin led them on as he explained. "Back in 79 AD, Mount Vesuvius erupted in ancient Italy, burying the cities of Pompeii and Herculaneum with hot mud and ash. There was a library in Herculaneum filled with papyrus scrolls that were buried until the eighteenth century, when they were discovered once more, black and carbonized. They were impossible to read. The prize was launched to find a way and three young scientists won, using a combination of scanning technology and AI large language model analysis to reveal the long-hidden texts."

Tenzin stopped in front of a wooden door, placing one hand on its smooth surface. "I can only pray we will get access to such technology so we can read the wonders that lie within this place."

He pushed open the door.

It was dimly lit, and Morgan's vision took a moment to adjust. Racks of wooden shelves stretched to the high ceiling, each filled with boxes marked with colorful cloth, now faded with age. It smelt of leather and old paper with an edge of incense.

"This way," Tenzin whispered, and even that soft sound was swallowed up in the vast library.

He led them on, walking with reverence alongside the rows of stacked manuscripts.

Morgan looked up at the sacred texts and wished, as she had so many times before on ARKANE missions, that she could stay here and learn about the place and its people.

What secrets might be discovered as the scrolls were digitized and translated? Much of it would be administrative, of course, the minutiae of daily life in the palace. But surely somewhere in here, there was something surprising, perhaps even something miraculous.

Tenzin opened another door at the end, revealing a room with modern-looking books and manuscripts.

"These records date from the 1940s, which I believe is what you're looking for?"

Morgan nodded. "Yes, we want to look at anything related to the Nazi expedition of 1938 when the regent at the time welcomed German scientists from the Ahnenerbe, the department for Ancestral Heritage."

Tenzin frowned. "A dark period of history indeed."

He crossed to a filing cabinet and rifled through a card index filled with handwritten notes. "The German team worked in these rooms, after being welcomed into the heart of the palace because they came with a swastika banner. We didn't know then what it would come to represent for Europe, but to Tibetans, the swastika has always been a symbol of well-being and good fortune. It can also represent the sun and prosperity, as well as love and mercy. I think perhaps that led our regent at the time to trust and welcome those men, although of course, their behavior here was quite odd."

"What do you mean?" Jake asked.

"One scientist, Bruno Beger, was an anthropologist. He was always measuring people's skulls, taking endless notes on the shape of their bodies, and he even made face masks of Tibetans. He was obsessed with our racial characteristics."

Morgan shivered as she thought of the SS officer's particular obsession with the human body, which Martin's research had expanded on. On Beger's return to Germany, the anthropologist had been responsible for an unusual skull collection, authorized by Himmler. Beger hand-selected subjects during his visits to concentration camps, essentially killing to order for his macabre collection. He was eventually convicted of eighty-six counts of accessory to murder during the Nuremberg trials of 1946, and it was chilling to think of him here in this room, even so many years ago.

The crimes of the past echoed through history, but for the Tibetans, it was the annexation of Tibet by the Chinese in 1950 that became the pivot point of their heritage in modern times. Perhaps there would still be a clue buried here as to what the Ahnenerbe team might have done with the fragment of the Spear they carried.

Tenzin held up a card from the index. "This shows that the period you want to look at is held in one of the smaller rooms. I'll show you through."

He led them on through a maze of ancient stacks, surrounded by manuscripts piled high around them. A wealth of knowledge unrealized, at least for now.

After guiding them through several more rooms, Tenzin pushed open a door and ushered them into a room with a faded mural of the palace on one wall, more shelves full of books, and several wooden chests on the floor.

"I don't know exactly where the records are, but it's almost certain they're in here."

A sudden sound of muffled shouting came from one of the rooms they had passed through.

Tenzin frowned. "I'll go and see what's happening. Start looking and I'll return when I can. Hurry now. You might not have much time."

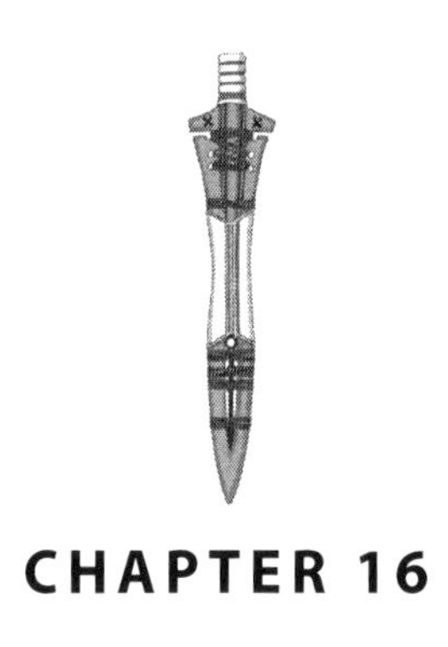

CHAPTER 16

TENZIN PULLED THE DOOR softly shut behind him.

Jake raised an eyebrow. "He's 'almost certain' the records are in here?"

Morgan bent to examine one of the shelves. "We'd better start looking then."

"What exactly are we searching for?"

"Letters maybe, a diary — anything written in German rather than Tibetan that might give us a clue to where the Spear fragment might be."

Jake scanned the shelves, reaching up to check labels on the books.

Morgan opened one of the juniper chests and the aromatic scent of the wood rose into the air. Inside lay a bundle of letters, tied with colorful twine.

She knelt down to check them, but they were in English, official letters from the time of the British occupation of India to the south. She lifted them out and checked beneath, but it was all bureaucratic government correspondence.

Jake stood examining the faded mural of the palace with its labyrinthine portrayal of the ancient library.

He traced the lines with a fingertip. "Morgan, look at this. There's German writing on this map, marking a particular place in the archives."

He bent closer. "It looks like *heilig*."

"Holy," Morgan whispered. "The palace certainly wasn't holy to the SS, so perhaps the map points the way to something they considered more precious."

The shouting outside grew louder.

It could be Chinese military or perhaps Gabriel's team. Whoever it was, they were getting closer.

Morgan considered their options. If they stayed here, they would be trapped in this room, at the mercy of whoever was coming.

There was nothing Tenzin could do to help them, and Morgan didn't want to get him into trouble for giving them access. They needed to get out of here now.

She snapped a picture of the mural. It was worth checking out and they could always return here later once it was quiet again.

Jake, already a step ahead of her, softly pulled open the door and checked the hallway. "It's clear."

Morgan followed him out and together, they headed deeper into the ancient stacks.

As the sound of shouting grew louder behind them, Morgan and Jake darted away into the serpentine hallways of the ancient Potala Palace. They moved quietly, almost sliding across stone floors worn smooth by the passage of time and the countless footsteps of learned monks over generations.

As they ventured deeper into older sections, the shelves they passed were made of dark, polished wood, intricately carved with traditional Tibetan motifs: dragons, lotus flowers, and symbols of the endless knot.

Each shelf was laden with texts of all sizes, from small, palm-sized prayer books to large, voluminous manuscripts, each carefully wrapped in cloth or protected by wooden covers inlaid with sacred symbols. There were scrolls, rolled and tied with colored ribbons, their edges frayed and the script faded, their meaning obscured by time.

Morgan tried to navigate the stacks with the picture of the mural on her phone, turning left and right, sometimes doubling back between the confusing levels of the library. It had clearly never been planned, but added to with each generation. Some walls were thick and structurally separate, but others were made from bookshelves, with gaps through into hidden alcoves and recesses.

Intricate murals and thangkas, Buddhist paintings, decorated the exterior walls, their vibrant colors dulled by the years but still magnificent, telling stories of deities, demons, and the eternal cycle of life and death.

Morgan and Jake navigated the dense forest of knowledge through the towering shelves, inhaling the heavy scent of aging wood and leather mixed with the sharp tang of ink.

They were close to the far exterior wall of the palace now, and tiny windows cast a dim light over the unending shelves of books. As they drew closer to the 'holy' mark on the mural map, Morgan slowed the pace, and together, they examined the stacks more closely for any sign of the sacred.

They rounded a corner to find a wooden door nestled into one corner, hung with rusted iron chains in a circular mandala pattern.

"Looks promising." Jake pushed against it, and the door creaked open.

The room was dim, with the only light coming from a high round window and a single flickering butter lamp, which cast sinister shadows over the face of a goddess.

But this was no serene divinity.

The statue depicted a monstrous, contorted figure wearing the skins of her human victims. She devoured a brain from the bloody skull she clasped in her twisted fingers, while leaping flames and portrayals of disease and death surrounded her.

"Not quite what I expected," Jake noted. "Seems a little at odds with how Tibet is usually portrayed."

Morgan shrugged. “Violence and death are just facets of humanity, and the gods reflect aspects of us. It’s clear that some still call on this goddess to protect Lhasa from invaders, but why did the German map lead here?”

Jake pointed at the images of skulls and corpses surrounding the goddess. “Seems like a good fit for the death-obsessed SS officers. Who is she, anyway?”

Morgan examined the statue more closely, recalling Martin’s notes on the palace. “I think it’s Palden Lhamo, a wrathful deity, considered by some as the queen of demons. When she died, she was sent to hell but fought her way back out, bringing with her a bag of disease and violent forms of death. But she also carried the power to cure and heal.”

As she considered the possibilities, Morgan felt a surge of hope. The legend of the Spear told of a neutral power that could be called on for good or evil, and used for death or life, killing or healing, balancing the same dichotomy as the goddess. A most appropriate place to leave the Spear fragment.

“Maybe there’s something behind it.” As she inched around the side, Morgan knocked against the statue.

It moved a little.

She reached out to steady it, sensing a warmth within the wood from the lamps or the years of worship that had seeped into the skin of the goddess. Morgan felt a strange kinship with her, a sense that this ancient being would have understood the dark curse that now lay in her own blood, and would not strike her down for moving one of her physical forms.

She looked over at Jake. “Help me shift her.”

Together, they edged the statue to one side, revealing a sunken niche in the floor. It was just big enough to hold a red leather diary, stamped with the stark runes of the SS.

Morgan knelt and picked it up. It was heavier than expected.

She carefully opened the book to find it hollowed out, the perfect size for the shard of ancient metal that lay within. A metal fragment of the Spear of Destiny, ringed by copper wire, sanctified by this altar of shadows.

The sound of running feet came from the corridor beyond.

Morgan quickly slammed the book shut and stuffed it into her bag as the door to the shrine opened.

Tenzin rushed in. “We have to go. Now. There are American soldiers looking for you and when you weren’t in the 1940s archive, they spread out. I managed to slip away. Come on!”

As Tenzin turned away, Morgan pushed the statue back over the hidden niche, disguising any evidence of what had been here.

Tenzin led Morgan and Jake quickly along the back wall of the palace, through a small doorway, and down a narrow flight of stairs, lit only by an occasional slit window.

The stairs seemed to go on forever, and Morgan heard Jake stop several times behind her to stretch his muscles.

Just as her quads started to spasm, they made it to the bottom.

Tenzin opened another door into a nondescript alleyway at the back of a market stall selling hand-carved prayer wheels with metal drums and colorful beads.

The shopkeeper paid them no heed, and Tenzin led Morgan and Jake away into the busy market where they soon blended in with tourist groups and locals shopping.

Once they were far enough away from the palace, Tenzin stopped on the edge of a main road. “Did you find what you were looking for?”

Morgan nodded. “I think so.”

He smiled. “Then please tell Martin. I’m happy to repay his many acts of helpful friendship.”

“I’ll be sure to pass on your kind words.” Morgan’s phone

buzzed in her pocket, and she pulled it out to check. "Here's a message from him now. There's a private plane with clearance from the Chinese military to take off toward India, where we can transfer on."

Tenzin raised a hand to hail a taxi and spoke rapidly to the driver. "He will take you to the airport."

Morgan gave a little bow. "Thank you for your help, Tenzin."

"*Thu-chi che,*" Jake said.

Tenzin smiled, pressed his hands together, and nodded. "May your travels be safe across the mountains."

The taxi took them to the airfield. Chinese soldiers waved them straight through, and Morgan was grateful for whatever strings Director Marietti must have pulled to get them out of here so swiftly.

As the plane took off, Morgan looked back one last time at the mountains of Tibet, hoping to return sometime and spend longer exploring the fascinating place with its ancient cultural heritage.

She pulled out her phone again, reading the more extensive notes from Martin. Thankfully Gemma's condition hadn't worsened, and the doctors were still working on further tests. Martin had also traced the soldier, Gabriel, from the records at Wewelsburg, along with the man who was ultimately responsible.

Morgan turned her phone so Jake could see the image of the patrician general on her screen. He was in full military uniform with rows of medals on his chest, and he stared into the camera lens with unshakeable authority. "This is the man behind the soldiers on our tail. General Ezekiel Stronghold."

Jake gave a low whistle. "Seriously? Isn't he the favorite to win the next US election?"

Morgan nodded. "That explains why he's so keen to find the pieces of the Spear. He must want a fallback option should he lose — and perhaps access to its power if he wins.

Apparently, he's hinted at powerful symbolism in his rally speeches. He also has his own elite force, Jericho Command."

"But there's still one piece of the Spear remaining, right?" Jake said. "We have two now and the General must have the other."

Morgan nodded. "Martin suggests that there's really only one other option to try. The place where the Nazi archives are held, where the original film of the Tibet expedition lies hidden, and where the documents taken from Hitler's Berlin bunker are stored."

CHAPTER 17

GABRIEL BLACKTHORN STRODE THROUGH the halls of Jericho headquarters, his boots pounding against the polished concrete floor with each purposeful step. The familiar corridors, once a source of pride and belonging, now felt suffocating.

After he had failed to retrieve the fragment of the Spear in Tibet, Gabriel had spent the journey back reflecting on why it might be so important, and questioning why the general wanted a religious relic that had been so important to the Nazis. It was not a cause Gabriel wanted to associate with, and yet he was starting to see parallels in the general's campaign that were too close for his liking. Doubts that had begun as a trickle now surged through him like a raging river.

Gabriel reached the conference room, where a closed meeting was in session. The heavy oak door loomed before him and he hesitated for a moment, his hand hovering over the handle as he questioned the wisdom of confrontation.

General Stronghold had been like a father to him, had shepherded his military career and given him purpose at Jericho Command, but Gabriel could no longer ignore the unease that gnawed at his gut. He had to know the truth, no matter the cost.

With a deep breath, he burst through the door.

The general stood at the head of the long conference table with other military leaders and politicians gathered around, thick folders in front of them brimming with documents. A screen on the wall displayed a map with what looked like a plan for troop movements and engagement with enemy forces in a war that had yet to occur.

The general turned at the intrusion. "Gabriel, we're in a meeting. Can it wait?"

Gabriel stood his ground. "It's urgent. We need to talk. Alone."

The general's jaw clenched, a flicker of annoyance crossing his features before he turned to the assembled group. "If you'll excuse me. I won't be long. The plan continues on page twenty-five. We can discuss the next steps on my return."

He walked out of the conference room, gesturing Gabriel to his private office a few doors down.

Once inside, the general closed the door and leaned back against the edge of the desk, his arms crossed over his chest.

"Well, then. What is it? What was so pressing that you felt the need to barge into a critical strategic meeting?"

Gabriel's hands curled into fists at his sides as he tried to calm the tension in his body. Some part of him still held a desperate hope that he was wrong about the man before him.

"I need to know the truth. About the Spear, about the mission. No more lies. No more half truths."

The general rose slowly and stood to his full height, his presence filling the room like a gathering storm. "You forget yourself, Gabriel. You swore an oath of loyalty to me, to Jericho Command, to our cause. The mission far outweighs any personal doubt. I'm disappointed that you, of all people, after all these years together, should question me. Where's your loyalty?"

Gabriel stood his ground, the weight of the general's

disappointment and anger pressing down on his shoulders. He swallowed hard, but he refused to back down.

"If being loyal means blindly following orders, without question or conscience, then maybe I've been loyal to the wrong cause all along. Are your intentions for the Spear as pure as you claim? Or is your personal ambition driving us all to destruction?"

The words hung in the air, a challenge that struck at the core of their relationship.

The general slammed his hand against the desk in fury, the sound reverberating through the room like a thunderclap. The force of the impact sent a tremor through the ancient texts and artifacts that lined the shelves.

"How dare you question my devotion to the cause? I've dedicated my life to this mission, like my father before me, and his father before him."

Gabriel took a step closer. "Then tell me the truth about the Spear. Is it just a talisman, some kind of symbol for those who believe? Why do you want it so much?"

The general turned to his bookshelf, to the ancient texts, as if taking strength from their historic pages.

"The Spear — once intact — can summon and harness great power. It holds the key to unlocking a new world we can build on the foundation of this broken country. It promises military might and a victory that the greatest armies cannot stand against."

The weight of the general's words settled like a leaden mass in Gabriel's chest as he considered the scope of such a war, the innocent lives lost.

"And you think you can wield that power? Control it? Harness it for the greater good?"

The general nodded. "I am the only one who can. The only one with the strength and conviction to see our mission through to the end. The world is ever more chaotic, and our adversaries clamor at the gates. Our country must be strong again, and with the Spear, our forces will prevail. You will stand by my side at the head of our army, Gabriel. It is your rightful place. It's what I've been grooming you for all these years since I discovered your abilities. I'm sorry I kept it from you, but now you know, we can forge this future together."

Gabriel took a step back, his mind reeling at the implications.

The general reached out to grasp his arm, drawing him closer. "Don't you see? With the Spear, we can usher in a new era. We can make the changes needed to align the country once more, and remove those who stand against us."

Gabriel shook off his grip. "Remove? What do you mean?"

The general shrugged. "There are… solutions to consider, of course. Those final details will be worked out. But first, we must assemble the Spear, then win the White House — with those objectives accomplished, I will reveal my plans to you in more detail."

Gabriel considered the map of invasion he had glimpsed in the conference room, the mania of power that lurked beneath the general's vision, the hubris that could lead them all to ruin.

He saw a future unfold, with General Stronghold at the head of an army, Spear in hand, marching over the bodies of fellow Americans and countless more, in a river of blood that could not be stopped.

Gabriel backed toward the door. "No. I won't be part of it. That kind of power cannot be contained."

The general snarled. "You would stand against me? Against the cause you swore to serve, the family you belong with? You are nothing without Jericho Command. Without me. You are just a lost soul, a broken weapon."

Gabriel flinched at the venom in his former mentor's words, but it solidified his resolve and made him sure that he didn't belong here.

"I may be broken, but I'm not lost. Not anymore."

Gabriel had a final choice. With his preternatural abilities, he could kill the general right now. Break his neck and end it all. But Stronghold had given him a life and a purpose in Jericho Command. Despite everything, he still loved the man like a father. He could not raise his hand against him, and Stronghold knew it.

But he had to get out — and quickly.

Gabriel spun around and strode out of the office.

Alarms blared to life behind him, their shrill cry piercing the air as Jericho Command soldiers mobilized to stop him escaping.

Gabriel raced through the familiar corridors, heart pounding, adrenalin coursing through his veins as he sought a clear escape route.

He ducked into a stairwell, taking the steps down two at a time.

He emerged onto the ground floor, his senses on high alert as the scent of gun oil and sweat hung heavy in the air. Gabriel moved forward cautiously, knowing what lay beyond.

But it was the only way out.

He rounded the corner, finding himself face to face with a wall of armed soldiers, their weapons trained on him with unwavering precision.

These were faces he knew, men and women he had trained with, fought beside, and trusted with his life. But now, their eyes held a mixture of confusion and hostility, their loyalty to Stronghold overriding all hesitation.

There was still time to stop, surrender, ask for forgiveness. He could be part of the family again.

But Gabriel knew his time at Jericho Command was over and every second that passed, every bullet fired, severed another thread of his connection.

In a burst of speed, he charged, moving with pure instinct.

He zigzagged across the hallway, his movements a blur of controlled chaos as he evaded the hail of gunfire that erupted around him. Bullets whizzed past his head, their heat searing his skin and leaving the acrid scent of burnt hair in their wake.

Gabriel pulled his gun, returned fire.

But even in the midst of battle, he avoided kill shots. These were still his people, misguided as they might be. He aimed for legs, arms, shoulders — anything to disable but not destroy.

A round grazed his shoulder, the impact spinning him slightly as he felt the hot, wet flow of blood soaking into his shirt.

He used the pain as fuel, launched himself over a bank of lockers, using the metal surface as a springboard to gain height and momentum.

He twisted in mid-air, his body contorting as he avoided another burst of gunfire. He landed in a roll, coming up firing, his aim true despite the chaos that swirled around him.

Gabriel vaulted over a fallen soldier, his feet barely touching the ground before he was moving again. His senses stretched out, mapping the flow of battle, anticipating the next attack, his speed and agility far beyond the capabilities of a normal human.

He disarmed one soldier with a flick of his wrist, sending the weapon clattering to the floor. Another he dispatched with a precise strike to a nerve cluster, sending them crumpling to the ground, unconscious.

But for every soldier he disabled, another seemed to take their place, pouring into the corridor, a tide of black tactical gear and determined faces. Gabriel couldn't keep this up forever.

He had to get out before he was overwhelmed by sheer numbers.

With a final burst of speed, he launched himself toward a huge picture window. He tucked his head down, his arms shielding his face as he braced for impact.

Gabriel smashed through the window in a glittering cascade of razor-edged fragments, a deadly kaleidoscope that tore at his skin and clothes.

He plunged to the ground below and hit the ground in a roll, his momentum carrying him across the manicured lawn, glass shards slicing at his exposed flesh.

He rolled to his feet and ran on, putting distance between himself and his pursuers. The grounds of the base stretched out before him, a maze of buildings and training facilities he knew intimately. But now, that familiarity was a double-edged sword.

Every corner, every shadow, held the potential for an ambush. His former comrades knew these grounds as well as he did, and they could use that knowledge against him.

Gabriel's mind raced. He needed a vehicle, something fast and rugged that could get him clear of the base. The motor pool was his best bet, but it lay on the far side of the compound, through a gauntlet of potential danger.

The crack of a sniper rifle split the air, the bullet whining past Gabriel's ear close enough he could feel the heat of its passage.

He dodged to one side, his movements more instinct than conscious thought.

Another shot, then another, each one closer than the last.

Gabriel ran, his legs pumping as he dodged and weaved, his enhanced reflexes the only thing keeping him ahead of the deadly rain of bullets.

His lungs burned, his muscles screamed in protest, but he pushed on.

The motor pool loomed ahead, a collection of armored vehicles and tactical SUVs gleaming in the early morning light.

He skidded to a halt, scanning the area, noting a mechanic working on a heavily reinforced Humvee. The engine was already running.

He sprinted over and swung the man away, spinning him across the ground as he jumped in and slammed the vehicle into gear. The tires spun on the concrete as Gabriel floored the accelerator.

The Humvee leapt forward, crashing through the flimsy barrier of the motor pool gate. Bullets pinged off the armor as the pursuing soldiers advanced.

The gates of the base loomed ahead, a last obstacle between him and the open road.

Gabriel didn't hesitate.

With a roar of the engine and a screech of rubber on the road, he smashed through the barrier.

As the base receded into the distance, he glanced in the rearview mirror. The soldiers would be on his tail soon enough.

Gabriel pressed down on the accelerator, heading back to the city.

He had to stop the gathering storm before Stronghold unleashed a rain of blood and fire, but he couldn't do it alone.

CHAPTER 18

THE TAXI PULLED UP IN front of the Thomas Jefferson Building of the Library of Congress, its neoclassical facade just one of many impressive structures in this area of Washington, DC.

As Jake paid the fare, Morgan stepped out onto the sidewalk, the small pack she carried now containing both Spear fragments wrapped in the tea towel from Wewelsburg. She moved to one side to avoid a group of students carrying Stronghold campaign banners toward the Capitol grounds on the other side of the road. It would be some kind of irony if the final piece of the Spear lay within the grounds of the library, only a few hundred meters from where the General had given his rallying speeches, and where crowds gathered again today to hear him speak.

Morgan turned to look up at the building's grand entrance. It was flanked by Corinthian columns adorned with acanthus leaves, which in the Ancient Greek tradition represented healing and life. But Morgan felt a sense of foreboding as she considered the Christian symbolism of the leaves, representing pain, punishment — and death.

The grandeur of the building echoed the opulence of Vienna, where architecture remained as a reminder of a once-powerful empire. Like the last years of the Austro-

Hungarian dynasty, the United States seemed also to be teetering on the brink of decline, its once unassailable power eroded by internal strife and external threat.

"Penny for them?" Jake asked as he joined her.

Morgan shook her head. "Nothing of any significance, at least not yet. Let's go inside."

Together, they climbed the stairs and passed through the massive bronze doors, stepping into the Great Hall. It was a symphony of marble and light, with a vaulted ceiling soaring overhead with so many layers of literary symbolism, it was hard to know what to look at first.

It reminded Morgan of a Catholic cathedral, with scholarly symbols in place of religious icons. The names of influential thinkers and artists were inscribed in gilded letters along the walls — Shakespeare, Michelangelo, Plato — next to illustrated quotes from literature. Statues of ancient scholars and philosophers gazed down from their pedestals, stone faces forever frozen in contemplation, and intricate mosaics on the floor depicted the signs of the zodiac. The architects of the library were clearly determined to pack in every possible way to illuminate the importance of learning and wisdom.

They passed beneath an arch inscribed with words from the poet Muriel Rukeyser: 'The universe is made of stories, not of atoms.' Morgan considered her own life as a tapestry woven from the threads of countless tales of love and loss, betrayal and redemption. Each mission, and each relic she pursued, added another chapter to the saga of her existence. She could only hope that Gemma's thread would not be severed too soon.

Jake pointed out a sign for the Rare Book and Special Collections Reading Room. "Looks like that's where we need to go."

They followed the signs, walking deeper into the maze of hallways, their footsteps echoing on the polished floor as they passed a series of murals depicting the evolution of the written word. From the crude pictograms of ancient civilizations to the illuminated manuscripts of medieval monks, the images told a story of humanity's unending quest for understanding.

Morgan stopped in front of a scene from the Library of Alexandria, the legendary repository of knowledge in ancient Egypt. Scholars in flowing robes pored over scrolls and codices, their faces lit by the flickering light of oil lamps. In the background, the ominous glow of flames hinted at the library's tragic end.

Knowledge was always a threat to those in power, and even now, in this supposedly free country, certain texts were banned by schools and libraries. Some groups even burned books, echoing the Nazis in 1933 as the authorities tried to control what people read and thought. But ideas had a way of escaping the flames. Perhaps she and Jake would find something here in what remained after the fires of war that might point to the last fragment of the Spear.

They reached the entrance to the Rare Book Room, its door guarded by a stern-faced attendant.

Morgan stepped forward to present their credentials just as a young African American woman emerged from an office at one side of the attendant's desk. She had a warm, inviting smile and her dark eyes sparkled with intelligence and curiosity.

"Welcome to the Library of Congress. I'm Brianna, Head Curator of the Special Collections. ARKANE Director Marietti sent me the details of your research, and I've pulled some boxes that might be relevant. Follow me."

Brianna led Morgan and Jake through a doorway into the Main Reading Room, the nondescript title a complete understatement for the grand rotunda they found themselves in.

A domed ceiling soared overhead, supported by gigantic

arches decorated with marble statues of ancient scholars gazing down on the modern students below. Desks ringed a central well, beyond which lay towering bookshelves, each one stretching from floor to ceiling, filled with an endless array of leather-bound volumes.

Every book was a window into a vanished world, a testament to the enduring power of the written word. But the sheer volume of knowledge was also daunting. There were not enough lifetimes to comprehend even the books within this one library, let alone the entire world of knowledge out there. The scale of it was breathtaking and Morgan was grateful they had Brianna to help them at least find a place to start.

Brianna led them on deeper into the heart of the library. The bustling hum of activity faded away, replaced by a profound stillness broken only by the soft whisper of their footsteps.

Finally, they reached a set of heavy wooden doors, the oak surfaces dull with the patina of age.

Brianna paused, her hand resting lightly on the ornate door handle. "These are the special collections where we keep the most precious books and treasures — and the most controversial."

She reached into the pocket of her cardigan and withdrew a heavy iron key, its surface worn smooth by years of use. She slid the key into the lock and turned it. The mechanism clicked, the sound echoing like a gunshot in the corridor.

Brianna pushed open the doors, and a wave of cool, dry air washed over them, carrying with it the scent of old paper and the faint tang of preservation chemicals.

They stepped into the dimly lit room, their eyes adjusting slowly to the low light. The space was smaller than Morgan had expected, more intimate and personal than the Main Reading Room. The shelves that lined the walls here were filled with boxes and crates, each one labeled with cryptic codes and faded inscriptions that hinted at secrets within.

Brianna walked to one shelf, her fingers running lightly over the labels until she found a particular spot.

"The Third Reich Collection holds thousands of individual items: books, papers, photographs, and film, much of it recovered from the salt mines where the Nazis hid their treasures, but also taken from Berlin. Hitler's own book collection is here. There's much to study if you had the time."

She hefted a small crate from the shelf and carried it over to a nearby table, setting it down with a gentle thud.

"Start with this, and I'll gather some other materials you might find useful about that dark period of history."

As Brianna gathered other boxes, Jake carefully removed the lid from the first. A stack of yellowed documents and faded photographs lay inside, nestled amidst layers of acid-free tissue paper. Jake reached in and carefully lifted out the top bundle. He checked through its contents, while Morgan took out the next layer.

They scanned the pages for any mention of the Heilige Lanze, or photos or sketches of the Spear.

As Brianna brought over more boxes and the minutes ticked by, Morgan felt the shadows of history gather in the corners of the room, the shades of dead men responsible for so much evil conjured from the ink-stained pages of the past.

Yet she felt a kind of perverse attraction to the forbidden knowledge, to the jagged edge between good and evil. A part of human nature wanted to learn about evil, however disturbing. To stare into the abyss and confront the darkest corners of the human soul. Was her curiosity stronger now after the curse, or was this part of who she had always been?

Brianna placed another box on the desk. "These papers are from the German scientists and intelligence officers recruited under Operation Paperclip, which might be relevant."

Jake frowned. "It's hard to believe the USA allowed so

many to escape the judgment of the Nuremberg trials, using research gained from torture and murder for their own purposes."

Brianna nodded gravely. "Yes, but then we have many disturbing chapters in our history, as does every nation. The rationale of Paperclip was that the scientific expertise was too valuable to lose, that we needed it to help us win the Cold War against the Soviets. One war begets another, and the cycle of violence turns the wheel of history once again." Brianna checked her watch. "I'm going to have to leave you to continue alone as I have another meeting. That's everything we have here, but I can call up other archives if you need them."

Brianna left the collections room as Jake and Morgan continued to rifle through the records.

Morgan opened the box from Operation Paperclip and picked up the journal that lay on top of a stack. It was embossed with golden initials and the distinctive eagle and swastika of the Nazi regime stamped on its cover.

She opened it to find dense scientific notations about various medical experiments. She flicked through the journal — then gasped at one of the pages.

Jake looked up from his investigation. "What is it?"

Morgan turned the journal to show him a hand-drawn sketch of a piece of the Spear of Destiny. "This journal belonged to a scientist, Kurt Blome. It looks like he was testing elements of the Spear for specific chemical properties, both for healing and also for use as a biological weapon."

Jake frowned. "The dual nature of the Spear would presumably allow for both, as the holder could use it for good or evil. What else does it say?"

Hurried footsteps suddenly echoed from the corridor outside.

The door burst open.

Morgan looked up, expecting to see Brianna once more.

But it was a man dressed in black, his gaze fixed upon her, the rune tattoo clear on his neck.

Gabriel Blackthorn.

"You both need to come with me. Now."

CHAPTER 19

MORGAN STARED AT GABRIEL, her heart pounding in her chest. What was he doing here? She had wanted to find him again, but not like this. She assessed his posture for any sense of threat while Jake reached for a heavy book to use as a makeshift weapon, clearly assuming this was about to get violent.

Gabriel raised his hands as if in surrender. "I'm here to help you. I'm not with Jericho Command anymore, but they're on the way. We have to get out of here."

He glanced over his shoulder, his body tense, then turned and gestured at Morgan's pack. "You have the Spear fragments?"

Morgan hesitated for a moment, her mind racing. Could she trust Gabriel? He was part of the very organization that hunted them. But something in his eyes, a flicker of desperation, told her he was risking everything to help them.

She made a split-second decision.

"Yes, and this might lead to one more." She grabbed the journal from the table and stuffed it into her pack.

"What the hell, Morgan?" Jake stood, arms crossed, his expression a storm about to break.

She reached out and touched his arm. "Please, Jake. I think we can trust him."

After a moment, Jake nodded, but he still glared at Gabriel with suspicion as they followed him out of the collections room.

Gabriel took the lead, and together they raced through the labyrinthine corridors of the library, their footsteps echoing on the polished floors as librarians and students alike scowled at their noisy passing.

They rounded a final corner near the emergency exit.

A sudden flurry of gunfire erupted.

Bullets whizzed past their heads, shattering the tranquil silence of the library.

"Get down!" Gabriel shouted, diving behind a towering stack of books.

Morgan and Jake crouched low as the hail of gunfire shredded ancient tomes, the violence somehow more shocking in this sanctuary of knowledge.

An alarm blared out as the acrid scent of shots fired filled the air.

Morgan pressed her back against the shelves, and Jake hunkered down next to her — both of them unarmed.

Gabriel peered around the edge of the bookcase, his gun drawn. "We're outnumbered. We need to find another exit. This way."

He ducked and sprinted off, moving swiftly and silently back through the stacks. Morgan and Jake followed close behind.

They entered a rare manuscripts room. Glass cases lined the walls, each containing a fragile piece of the past. Illuminated manuscripts, ancient maps, and delicate scrolls lay preserved behind protective shields, their secrets waiting to be unlocked.

Gabriel weaved through the maze of display cases, his movements precise and purposeful, a barely restrained power thrumming beneath his skin.

A shadow detached itself from behind a nearby case.

A figure clad in black tactical gear stepped in front of them, a gun aimed straight at Gabriel's heart.

"Don't move," the figure commanded, his voice cold and sharp as a blade.

Morgan's heart lodged in her throat. They were trapped, caught between their pursuers and this new threat.

But Gabriel didn't hesitate.

In a blur of motion, he lunged forward, slamming into the figure with brutal force. The two men grappled, their limbs a tangle of coiled muscle and deadly intent.

Gabriel fought with a savage grace, his every move a study in controlled violence. Once more, Morgan sensed the edge of the supernatural in his abilities.

With a final, brutal twist, Gabriel wrenched the gun from his opponent's grasp.

The man crumpled to the floor, his body limp and unmoving. But he still breathed and Gabriel quickly placed him in the recovery position, a sign of care for one of his old teammates.

He turned, chest heaving with exertion. "We need to find another way out. They must have all the exits covered."

Morgan nodded, her mind racing as she tried to recall the layout of the library. "There's a service elevator in the back. If we can reach it, we might be able to—"

A sudden burst of gunfire cut off her words as bullets tore through the room.

Glass cases shattered, the shards raining down, mingling with fragments of shredded ancient texts. Morgan ducked instinctively, her body slamming against the shelves as sharp splinters rained down around her. Jake sheltered a few meters away behind another display case.

Gabriel returned fire, his movements precise and controlled. He aimed for the legs, the arms, any non-lethal target that would take their pursuers out of the fight without causing permanent harm.

But Jericho Command was relentless.

They surged forward, a tide of black-clad figures that seemed to fill every inch of the library.

Hands grabbed Morgan's neck from behind.

She twisted in the grip and exploded up, breaking the hold and barreling into the soldier who had attacked her.

They grappled, limbs tangled in a desperate struggle for dominance.

But Morgan was faster, stronger, fueled by rage.

She twisted and wrenched a gun from the man's belt. She brought the butt of the weapon down on his temple with a sickening crack. He crumpled to the ground, limp and unmoving.

Morgan spun, gun outstretched, looking for Jake amidst the chaos.

She caught a glimpse of him, his muscular frame ducking and weaving as he fought off two Jericho Command operatives. His expression was a mask of grim determination, his fists flying in a blur of motion, but in the maelstrom, she couldn't get a clear shot at his attackers.

Two more figures emerged from the shadows and advanced upon him.

Jake was outnumbered.

Morgan charged across the room — but another soldier caught her and, with an outstretched arm, threw her spinning across the floor.

She leaned into the fall and rolled back up to her feet.

From across the room, she saw Jake go down under the weight of four soldiers. He struggled hard, thrashing as he fought to break free.

Morgan stood and fired, hitting one of his attackers in the arm.

But another pulled Jake up to his knees, arm around his neck, using him as a shield. She couldn't fire again without endangering him.

Jake gazed at her across the room with a desperate, pleading look that tore at Morgan's heart. He was urging her to stay back, to save herself, but she knew he would always fight for her, as she would for him.

The soldiers dragged Jake back outside the hall, the others covering their retreat with more gunfire.

Morgan gripped her weapon, readying herself to charge after Jake, no matter the cost.

But suddenly Gabriel was there with her, his voice low and urgent. "We have to run. We can't help Jake if we're captured, too, and we need to get the pieces of the Spear away."

Morgan wanted to argue, to fight, to tear the world apart until she brought Jake back to safety. But Gabriel was right. They had to keep moving and stay one step ahead of Jericho Command.

If the team had wanted to kill, the soldiers could have finished them all off. But clearly, it was a capture mission. There was still more to play for. They would keep Jake alive, and she would find out why soon enough.

Gabriel sprinted out of the room, and Morgan followed as they headed for the service area, zigzagging through the corridors as the alarm continued to shriek around them.

A few minutes later, they burst out of the back of the library and raced away into the streets beyond, darting between the growing crowds heading to rally at the Capitol. The sounds of sirens and shouting voices echoed in the distance, as they lost themselves in the backstreets of Washington, DC.

Gabriel led the way, and as they reached a residential area, he slowed to a walk as they recovered their breath.

Before they could discuss what happened, the shrill ring of Gabriel's phone pierced the air.

He pulled it out, his brow furrowing as he glanced at the screen. "It's Stronghold."

Gabriel met Morgan's gaze, a silent question in his eyes.

She nodded, steeling herself for whatever lay ahead. He answered the call, putting it on speaker.

"I have a proposition for you both. Whatever you found in the library is the key to the final piece of the Spear. Retrieve it and bring all the pieces to me at the Capitol, and Jake will be released unharmed. Or at least he'll be alive, with any injuries he might have sustained during capture."

Morgan felt a wave of nausea at the thought of Jake beaten and bloody, his life hanging in the balance, helpless against the brutality of Jericho Command.

"And if we don't bring it to you?" Gabriel asked.

"I think it's clear how this will end."

There was a dark promise in Stronghold's words before the line went dead.

"I'm doing what he asks," Morgan said immediately, well aware how easily Gabriel could take the pieces of the Spear from her and leave Jake to suffer and die.

She had one move left to play.

Morgan reached out a hand and touched Gabriel's arm, her bare skin against his. Electricity arced between them as it had in Vienna, and as his eyes widened, she gasped with the intensity.

But she didn't let go.

"There's something between us," Morgan whispered. "And I think I know why, Gabriel. I know where you come from. I know why you're different."

Gabriel pulled back, his fists clenched as he spun away from her.

He could easily force her to tell him, but Morgan was sure that the honorable side of him would prevail.

"I'll tell you everything once you help me get Jake back, and I promise, we'll find a way to stop Stronghold using the Spear. Please, Gabriel, I need your help."

He took a deep breath and closed his eyes, clearly wrestling with the desire to run from it all.

After a moment, he nodded. "What did you find in the library?"

Morgan reached into her pack and pulled out the scientific journal. She flipped through the pages until she found the picture of the Spear fragment and the associated test results.

"This scientist, Kurt Blome, was part of Operation Paperclip. His other records should be at Fort Detrick, the military compound focused on biomedical research and development where the scientists worked after the war."

Gabriel leaned in, quickly scanning the faded text and diagrams. "Detrick is a US Army Medical Command installation. It's not far from here, but I've never been inside. We'll need help to get clearance."

He ran a hand through his hair, his jaw clenching. "I might have a way, but it's not going to be easy."

* * *

As Gabriel considered their options, his former mentor's angry words echoed in his mind. The pull of loyalty to the man he had followed for decades was hard to resist, even after the revelation of what Stronghold intended to do with the assembled Spear.

Now he knew Morgan held knowledge of his past, and Gabriel would do much to learn the truth. Even risk his life to save a man he didn't know or care about. She clearly loved Jake, though, if she would give up the pieces of the precious relic and risk a global war for his sake.

There had to be a way to rescue Jake, and still stop Stronghold. The way forward wasn't clear, but they could only take one step at a time and see what emerged. Sometimes, the answer unfolded in the depths of a mission and perhaps, together, he and Morgan would find a way.

But first, they had to get into Fort Detrick.

With a heavy heart, he pulled out his phone and called Stronghold back.

“We’ll do it. But I need a helicopter and as much clearance as you can get for the labs at Fort Detrick.”

There was a moment of heavy silence on the other end of the line.

“Done.” Stronghold’s tone was clipped. “There’s a helipad at the hospital nearby. The chopper will drop you at Fort Detrick, but once you’re inside, you’re on your own. I need this clean, Gabriel.”

“Understood.” He ended the call and turned to Morgan. “Let’s go.”

As they made their way to the helipad, Gabriel couldn’t shake a sense of foreboding at the mission ahead, and the choice he knew must come.

While he had promised Morgan his help, Gabriel was resolute. He would not let Stronghold reassemble the pieces of the Spear — even if it cost his life, and that of Jake Timber.

CHAPTER 20

THE HELICOPTER RIDE WAS a short trip from Washington, DC to the military base over the state border in Maryland. As they took off, Morgan glimpsed the growing crowds gathering for the rally — their bright red banners standing out in the sea of people. It was too noisy to talk about a plan, but Morgan felt a strange sense of calm as the helicopter descended into Fort Detrick. Something about the bond she had with Gabriel made her confident they would figure out a way forward.

Both of them had enough military experience to trust each other's skills, and she was grateful that he was on her side this time, instead of the enemy. It was a temporary truce, though; she was sure of that. Gabriel wasn't doing this for Jake, and she would have to be careful once they made it out.

If they made it out.

The helicopter landed and Gabriel hurried away from the spinning blades; Morgan followed, squinting at the imposing buildings in the glare of the sun. While General Stronghold had authorized their landing, armed soldiers still surrounded the helipad. She and Gabriel might make it inside, but Morgan wondered how the hell they would get out again.

Gabriel strode toward the command post, Morgan by his side. They handed their credentials to the soldier on duty, who checked their details against his computer system before waving them inside.

"Welcome to Fort Detrick, Captain Blackthorn, Dr Sierra. Please report to the security desk and you'll be assigned an escort to take you into the military archives. Have a good day."

Together, they walked into the main administration building. Photos of military leaders hung on the walls alongside plaques denoting the casualties of various wars. Men and women in uniform strode past, and somewhere in the distance, Morgan could hear the rhythmic sound of marching feet.

The sound was reminiscent of the footage of the Nuremberg parade grounds as Hitler spoke to his soldiers before sending them out to war. He had intended to use the Spear for military might, and Morgan could only hope they might prevent a new generation from doing the same. No matter the colors of their flag, no nation should wield such a potentially powerful weapon again.

They checked in at the desk and were soon after greeted by their escort, a slim Asian American man with the earnest air of a lower-ranked soldier hoping to impress a senior officer.

"Welcome, Captain. I'm Corporal Kim. I'll escort you to the archives. This way."

After passing through security scanners, aware that cameras traced their path, Morgan and Gabriel followed Corporal Kim into the heart of the labyrinthine complex.

Down one corridor, they passed a sign for the US Army Medical Research Institute of Infectious Diseases (USAMRIID), and Morgan wondered how much of what they researched here now was based on scientific results procured from the Nazis.

Infectious diseases, bioweapons, engineered viruses, trauma research. All hard-won knowledge cut from the bodies of those experimented on in the camps. The victims were exposed to chemicals, radiation, environmental extremes, and deliberately inflicted violence. They were tortured, raped, and mutilated, treated as less than human for the sake of scientific advancement.

Of course, atrocities were still committed in the name of progress. Perhaps not here at Fort Detrick, but certainly at other military bases in nations that thought themselves better than the Nazis, yet treated certain groups in ways that were just as inhumane.

Corporal Kim stopped in front of a bank of elevators. "We need to go down into the basement."

They descended and emerged into a long corridor lined with nondescript doors. It was cold, with bright fluorescent lighting, and the air had a tinge of antiseptic.

"I was told to show you what remains of Kurt Blome's research lab." Corporal Kim stopped in front of one of the doors. He scanned his pass, the door clicked, and he pushed it open. "Everything is in here."

Morgan and Gabriel entered the room. The space was dimly lit, with only a few fluorescent bulbs casting an unsettling greenish glow across the scene. Tall glass cases, like those for museum exhibits, stood sentinel around the walls, their surfaces frosted with age and neglect.

The glass was thick and slightly distorted, obscuring the contents within. Morgan walked to one of the cases and wiped away a layer of dust with her sleeve, revealing stacks of boxes and scientific equipment piled haphazardly inside. The boxes were made of sturdy, reinforced cardboard, their labels faded and peeling, hinting at the long-forgotten experiments and research they once contained.

The next case enclosed a long work table strewn with an array of scientific equipment. Beakers, test tubes, and petri dishes lay scattered, some still containing the desiccated remains of long-dead samples. Bunsen burners and hot plates stood silent, their surfaces caked with the residue of countless experiments. A microscope, its lens cracked and clouded, lay on its side, a testament to the hasty abandonment of this once-thriving laboratory. It was as if the scientists had just walked out one day, leaving everything as it was, then it had been encased in glass to preserve what was left.

But Morgan couldn't shake the feeling that the cases served a dual purpose — protecting the lab from the ravages of time, from dust getting in, but perhaps also preventing something sinister from getting out.

Morgan twisted the latch on the case full of boxes, half expecting to find it locked, but the door swung open. Gabriel unlatched the case with the lab equipment, his movements careful and measured. Corporal Kim stood watch by the door, tracking their every move.

Morgan rifled through one box, her hands trembling slightly, as a sense of unease crawled up her spine. She pulled out a lab notebook, its pages yellowed and brittle with age. Page after page of meticulous notes and diagrams detailed Blome's experiments with nerve agents and chemical weapons. His cold-blooded calculations of the most efficient ways to harm and kill made her stomach churn, the clinical precision of his words a stark contrast to the horror his lab must have been.

She pushed the thoughts away and focused on the references to Blome's occult interests.

Cryptic lines about ancient artifacts and supernatural power were woven amongst the scientific jargon, hinting at a deeper purpose behind Blome's work. Photographs of ritual runes, sigils used to summon demons, and glyphs that spoke of blood magic lay tucked between pages of chemical formulas.

There must be something here.

Morgan delved deeper in the box, digging under the journals, her heart racing as she lifted a small box from the depths of Blome's archives.

It was made of weathered wood from an ancient oak, and its surface was etched with intricate symbols that seemed to writhe in the dim light of the lab. The surrounding air felt charged with an unseen energy that made the hairs on the back of her neck stand on end.

As she turned the box in her hands, Morgan realized it was a puzzle, its panels and hinges interlocked in an intricate way. The runes that covered its surface were not mere decoration, but clues to unlocking its secrets, preventing those without the right knowledge from gaining access.

But Morgan had seen those symbols before — in the ritual chamber under Wewelsburg Castle.

"Gabriel, come over here. I think this might be what we're looking for."

She thought back to the chamber, trying to remember the order of the runes around the walls. As she touched the box, the symbols seemed to shift, their meanings elusive and ever-changing, like curls of smoke from a ritual flame.

Morgan pulled out her phone, using the photos from the chamber to order the symbols. She turned the box, folding its panels back, until, with a final twist, it clicked open. The lid slid back with a soft sigh, and Morgan's breath caught in her throat as she peered inside.

Nestled on a bed of black velvet was a small, jagged piece of metal, its surface pitted and scarred as though it had been through the fires of hell.

The final piece of the Spear.

Morgan reached out to touch the shard — as Gabriel reached for it, too.

Their fingers touched on the metal.

A sudden flare of light erupted, a blinding flash that

seared Morgan's eyes and set every nerve in her body aflame.

She cried out in pain and surprise as the light coalesced into a swirling vortex of energy that tore at the fabric of reality.

Through the maelstrom, Morgan glimpsed another world that lay beyond the veil.

An army of demons marched across a blasted hell-scape, their twisted forms writhing in a dance of unholy ecstasy. A great city crumbled to dust before the horde as the screams of the dying echoed through the burning air. At the center of it all was the Spear of Destiny, made whole — and terrible in its power.

CHAPTER 21

As swiftly as the vision appeared, it blinked back into darkness, leaving both Morgan and Gabriel gasping for breath.

Corporal Kim rushed over. "Are you okay? What happened?" He reached for the phone at his belt. "I need to call this in."

Gabriel spun around and grabbed the corporal's arm.

At the threat, Kim went for his gun. With a speed that blurred the air, Gabriel swept the corporal's feet from under him, straddling the soldier and holding him down. He removed the gun from Kim's belt and pressed the soldier's face gently to the floor with enough force to keep the soldier quiet.

"I'm sorry, Corporal, but we need to take this box out of here. I can't have you calling it in."

While Morgan wasn't expecting such a move, Gabriel was right. There's no way Corporal Kim could let them leave with the box, not after he witnessed… whatever had emanated from it as well as their reaction. She didn't know what the hell just happened, but they could only find out if they escaped Fort Detrick without being detained, and time was running out for Jake.

She grabbed a coiled cable and handed it to Gabriel.

He gagged the corporal, bound his hands and feet, and then wrapped the cable around one end of a cabinet. "We'll radio your location after we get clear of the area. You won't be here long. But we have a deadline to meet and we don't have time to explain this now."

Morgan bent to check that Kim could breathe properly and the ties weren't hurting his skin. "I'm sorry," she whispered.

Gabriel grabbed the box from the table, and for a moment, Morgan felt an almost uncontrollable desire to take it from him. It was hers. She couldn't bear it in his hands. The longing was so extreme it took her breath away.

She blinked and shook her head. The fragment was clearly powerful indeed and it gave a sense of what the Spear might do, at least in the hands of someone with tainted blood — that which she and Gabriel shared.

"We need to get out of here." He put the box in his backpack, pulled open the door, and peered out into the corridor. He looked back at Morgan. "You ready?"

She nodded, her eyes flicking from his pack to meet his gaze. "Let's go."

They made their way back through the labyrinthine corridors of Fort Detrick, acting as normal as they could. Gabriel was outwardly calm, but he walked with a coiled intensity, his eyes scanning their surroundings, alert for any sign of trouble.

They approached the security checkpoint.

The guard eyed them with suspicion, his hand hovering near his weapon as he noted the absence of their escort. "Where's Corporal Kim?"

Gabriel shrugged. "He was called away on an urgent matter. But we're leaving now, anyway. I'm a captain." He showed his credentials. "Surely we don't need an escort to get back to the helipad."

The guard's eyes narrowed, his gaze flicking between

them, searching for any sign of deception. Morgan exhaled slowly, aware of the fragile balance that hung between them. One wrong move, one misplaced word, and they would be detained for questioning. Even with Gabriel's abilities, they couldn't fight their way out of this heavily guarded facility.

Gabriel held his ground, his voice steady and assured. "Check if you like, but we have a tight schedule to keep. I'm sure you understand."

For a tense moment, the guard hesitated, his finger tapping against the butt of his gun. Then with a curt nod, he waved them through. "Make sure you sign out at the front desk."

Gabriel inclined his head in acknowledgment. "Of course. Thank you for your cooperation."

They dropped their passes back and hurried to the helipad, the thrum of rotor blades starting up as they approached. Morgan almost expected armed soldiers to run toward them in a last-minute arrest, but the helicopter lifted off without incident, the ground falling away beneath them as they rose into the clear blue sky.

She let out a sigh of relief, her fingers unclenching from the edge of her seat as the adrenalin slowly ebbed from her system.

Opposite her, Gabriel sat with one hand gripping his pack tightly, the box hidden inside.

"We need to talk," he said, his voice low and intense, barely audible over the roar of the engines.

He handed her a headset and pulled another over his ears, switching them both to a private channel so the pilot couldn't listen.

Morgan indicated the pilot with a tilt of her head. "I presume he's taking us straight back to the Capitol, directly to Stronghold?"

Gabriel nodded. "We don't have much time." He took a deep breath. "What happened back there… the vision?"

"I saw it, too," Morgan said softly. "The Spear is more than just a piece of ancient metal. But I don't think its power is released for just anyone. The fact that it lay abandoned in the basement at Fort Detrick proves that."

"So why can we feel it? You need to tell me what you know, Morgan. I'll help you rescue Jake, but I need to know."

The helicopter banked sharply, turning toward the distant skyline of Washington, DC into a darkening sky. A storm was coming and clouds gathered above the dome of the Capitol, where a last ray of sun cast a shade of bloody crimson over its peak.

"On my last mission, I was cursed by an ancient creature, my blood somehow tainted by a demonic force." Morgan gazed out the window, imagining Gemma in the hospital bed back in Oxford. "Somehow its shadow struck down my niece — she's only a little girl — and I'm hoping that the Spear might somehow heal her."

Gabriel frowned. "I'm sorry for your niece, but that doesn't explain my abilities, or the fact there's something between us and the Spear."

Morgan pulled out her phone and found the photos from Wewelsburg, shuffling through to Gabriel's records. She handed it to him and as he read, his eyes widening, she tried to explain.

"Certain important Nazi officers were heavily into the occult. These pictures are from Himmler's castle, where we believe they attempted to summon demons into the bodies of elite SS soldiers." The words seemed absurd as Morgan spoke them aloud, but she pushed on.

She told Gabriel about the dark rituals in the crypt beneath the castle, of the demonic seeds planted in the wombs of abused women. Of the twisted experiments that sought to create a new breed of soldier, weapons forged in the fires of the occult, empowered by the Spear.

"The rituals have continued over generations, and it

looks like you were conceived there before being adopted here in the USA."

Gabriel swiped through the photos, his frown deepening. "You think I'm some kind of human-demon hybrid, or at least the descendent of someone who was?"

Morgan shrugged. "To be honest, I've seen so many unexplainable things on my ARKANE missions. I can't say for sure whether this is true or not, but how do you explain your abilities?"

Gabriel sighed and bit his lip. "Since I was a child, Stronghold has always told me that my skills are a gift from God, that I should embrace them and use them to serve my country. I've prayed so many times for the burden to be lifted… But perhaps God cannot hear the prayers of the damned."

His words were stricken with grief, and Morgan's heart wrenched at his obvious dismay. His faith must be rocked to the core by his dark lineage, but as she thought about it, a singular idea emerged.

"Perhaps Stronghold knows the truth of your birth? Perhaps he has known of it all along, and needs you to activate the Spear somehow."

Gabriel clenched his fist around the handle of his pack, knuckles white. "It's time to ask him."

The helicopter touched down on the hospital rooftop, the wind from its rotors and the gathering storm whipping Morgan's hair into a frenzy.

Gabriel was already moving, his long strides eating up the distance as he headed for the access door, the pack clutched tightly in one hand.

Morgan hurried after him, her gaze fixed on the precious package with the final piece inside. She couldn't let Gabriel hand the fragments over, or somehow be persuaded to wield the completed Spear. But she also needed to save Jake. She would not leave him behind.

As she crossed the threshold into the hospital and followed Gabriel down the stairs, her phone rang with the ring tone reserved for her sister.

She answered it quickly.

"Morgan, you need to come home." Faye's voice was distant with shock and grief. "The doctor says Gemma doesn't have much time. You need to come now if you want to see her before the end."

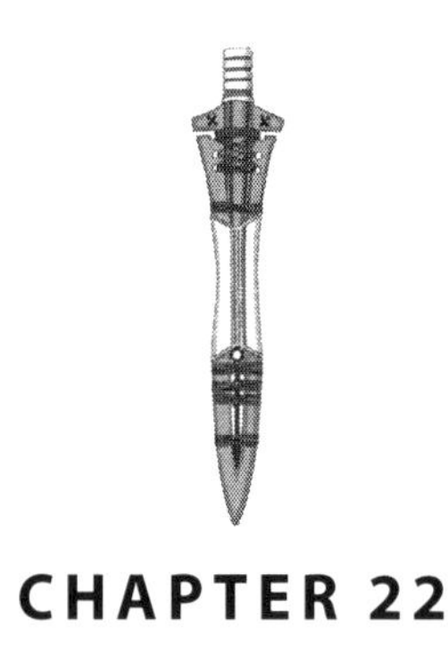

CHAPTER 22

Morgan's hand trembled as she ended the call, Faye's desperate words still echoing in her mind. She stood frozen, torn between her need to rush to Gemma's side, to be with her sister at this most terrible time — and the knowledge that Jake's life hung in the balance, his fate intertwined with the fragments of the Spear.

She could not go to them both.

Time slowed as she considered the impossible choice.

Gabriel turned on the staircase, noticing her dismay. "What is it, Morgan?"

"My little niece, Gemma. She's… she's dying. The doctors say she only has a short time left."

The words spoken aloud tasted like ashes on her tongue, bitter and acrid. Her mind recoiled at the image of Gemma's tiny body lost amidst a tangle of tubes and wires.

Gabriel jogged back up the steps, his gaze intense. "Listen to me. There's still a chance for Gemma — and for Jake. If we can unite the final pieces of the Spear, if we can unlock its power, and choose life for its purpose, perhaps we can save them both."

Morgan could hardly breathe as the weight of the decision squeezed her chest like a vise. She drew in a shuddering breath, picturing Faye at Gemma's bedside, each second a precious treasure slipping through her fingers like grains of sand. The agony of her sister's grief. The hollow ache of a future without her beloved niece. The thought was too much to bear.

But if she flew back now, Morgan could only sit and watch death take Gemma, and she would lose Jake as well. If there was even the faintest chance that the Spear could perform a miracle, that its ancient power could snatch Gemma back from the brink of oblivion, then Morgan had to try.

She reached into her bag and pulled out the two wrapped pieces of the Spear. The colorful tea towel seemed incongruous after the dark vision they had seen in the lab, but it at least contained the latent power of the shards within.

After a moment's hesitation, Morgan held the bundle out to Gabriel. "I choose life."

Gabriel met her gaze and placed his hands around hers over the bundle. "We can choose it together."

At his touch, Morgan felt the connection between them renewed as their blood harmonized in that strange way. There was something almost addictive about it, something she feared might become a compulsion if she let it.

He started to pull back, but Morgan clutched his hand once more. "We can't let the Spear become whole again. It might be too powerful, even for you."

Gabriel nodded. "Of course, but we have to go now."

Morgan relinquished the bundle and Gabriel put it alongside the box in his pack.

Together, they ran down the stairs and out onto the street, hailing a taxi to take them back to the heart of the city.

The driver slowed as they approached the Capitol grounds. The political rally had swollen to a massive size, spilling out and blocking the streets.

Morgan and Gabriel walked the last kilometer, weaving through the crowd, finally making it to Capitol Hill, now packed with thousands of people loyal to General Stronghold.

The sky above churned with storm clouds, swirling in a vortex of unnatural colors, as if streaks of pitch and flame tainted the sky. Lightning flickered within the depths of the clouds, its strength building.

A fierce wind whipped across the gathered crowd, swirling the banners emblazoned with Stronghold's face. Strident voices rose in a cacophony of chants and slogans, and Morgan sensed brutality and rage close to the surface. It wouldn't take much to ignite this pack to violence and the entire city would pay the price.

"We have to get inside," Gabriel shouted over the din. "Stay close. This way."

He guided her around the edge of the crowd to a doorway guarded by two Jericho Command soldiers.

One man saluted Gabriel as he approached, but the other stepped forward, his insolent gaze challenging his now-disgraced captain.

"The general's expecting you. This way."

Morgan's heart beat faster as she and Gabriel followed the soldiers through the grand foyer, their footsteps echoing on the polished marble floor. The eyes of long-dead presidents and politicians from both sides of the aisle seemed to follow their every move from the oil paintings that lined the walls.

They walked on through a maze of corridors, then down a spiral staircase into the depths below the Capitol.

The stone was older here, far more ancient than that of the grand buildings above, and the air was cold, with a mineral edge. The corridor narrowed as they wound deeper and deeper, until finally they reached a massive set of copper double doors.

The first soldier stepped forward and placed his hand on the ancient metal, his lips moving in a silent incantation.

He pushed at the doors and, with a grating creak, they swung open.

Morgan followed the soldier into a cavernous chamber,

Gabriel close behind. The walls were hewn from rough, ancient stone, revealed by the flickering dance of light cast by flaming torches held by soldiers at the edges of a gathered crowd.

The place had clearly been constructed with the crypt of Wewelsburg Castle in mind. The same runes were inscribed on the walls, conjuring the same malevolent energy. A chamber ripped from the pages of dark history, a twisted reflection of the atrocities committed half a world away and generations before.

Military commanders from each of the services stood before a central dais, along with high-ranking politicians, wealthy business leaders, and even some celebrities. They were the elite, the chosen few, their loyalty bought with promises of power and privilege in the new world order that would come after the inevitable chaos.

General Ezekiel Stronghold stood before them all on the dais in front of a gleaming black altar, a sacred flame burning in a silver bowl upon it. The general wore full military regalia with an array of medals on his chest. A silver and gleaming black onyx death's head ring glinted on his finger.

Stronghold embodied the spirit of war, and Morgan sensed the latent power in him. With the completed Spear in hand, this nation would follow him into global conflict without question.

"Our guests are here." The general's deep voice echoed through the chamber as he pointed at Morgan and Gabriel. The crowd turned to look, and Morgan saw a perverse hunger in their eyes, a desire for blood to be shed and power to be summoned.

"Bring him."

At Stronghold's words, two soldiers marched out of the darkness behind the altar, dragging Jake between them. He was barely conscious, his face a mess of bruises and blood, his clothes covered in dark stains.

He lifted his head with a herculean effort, his gaze meeting Morgan's across the chamber with an intensity that took her breath away.

In that moment, in the depths of his pain and despair, she knew he was telling her to run. To save herself.

It was in the set of his jaw, and the flicker of determination that still burned in his eyes despite everything he had endured.

Morgan started toward him, but before she could take more than a single step, the soldiers were upon her. They grabbed her arms, holding her back.

"Jake!" she shouted, struggling against them, twisting in a futile attempt to get away.

Gabriel reached out a hand and touched her arm. "Wait," he whispered, and in his voice, she heard a dark promise.

Morgan took a deep breath and stopped struggling.

"Give me the other pieces of the Spear, and you can have him," Stronghold called out over the heads of the gathered faithful.

Gabriel stood motionless, clutching the bag containing the Spear fragments, his knuckles white with the force of his grip.

His gaze locked onto Stronghold's, his eyes as hard as tempered steel, his expression a mask of barely contained fury. Coiled energy radiated from him, a primal rage like a berserker of Viking days on the brink of unleashing total destruction.

Yet he remained silent, a wordless challenge that hung heavy in the air.

The moment stretched into an eternity, a tense, suffocating beat — before Gabriel released his hold on the bag, his fingers uncurling with deliberate, almost insolent slowness.

The soldier behind him snatched it up and carried it to the dais, handing it over to Stronghold with a bow.

The general placed it on the stone altar, opened the bag, and pulled out the pieces of the Spear.

"You have what you want," Morgan called out. "Let Jake go."

Stronghold chuckled, and his laugh seemed all the more sinister for its edge of unbridled joy.

More soldiers emerged from the shadows, their forms coalescing out of the darkness, until Morgan and Gabriel were surrounded by a ring of unforgiving steel.

"Blood empowers the Spear," the general said. "The first drop wakens its dormant power, and the second — the greater sacrifice — unleashes it. Carnage and chaos will reign, but first, the blade must be restored." He nodded to his men. "Bring him."

Two soldiers dragged Jake to the stone altar, its surface stained and pitted with dark, rusty residue. He struggled against his captors, but he was no match for the men who forced him down onto the cold, unyielding stone.

They strapped him in place with heavy chains and ripped open his shirt, baring his chest before the general.

The assembled congregation began to chant, voices rising in discordant harmony. The words were ancient, guttural, a language that seemed to writhe and twist upon the tongue. It spoke of dark ritual and souls consumed by an ancient weapon empowered by the blood of the divine — or the demonic.

Shadows in the corners of the chamber began to shift, taking on substance and solidity. They pooled together, gathering in corners and crevices, forming silhouettes with peaked caps, swastika armbands, and the leering skull of the death's head gleaming from their silver rings. The elite of the Third Reich summoned forth, a legion of the damned, called to bear witness to this unholy rite.

The general laid the fragments of the Spear in front of the silver fire bowl. With the replica from the Vienna treasury as the central piece, he held the first fragment in the flame until the copper wire glowed, then attached it to its rightful place as he uttered words of power, his voice a guttural growl.

As he repeated the action with each piece, the shadows in the chamber thickened, the atmosphere growing heavy with malevolence until finally, the completed blade gleamed with a dull, ominous light, its edges jagged and cruel.

Stronghold held it high before the gathered faithful. "After generations, the Spear is complete once more, and now, our glorious future can begin."

He raised the Spear above Jake's heart.

"No!" The scream tore from Morgan's throat, a primal, anguished cry, swallowed by the chanting of the assembled congregation as it rose to a fever pitch.

Morgan fought against the soldiers holding her, muscles straining, but they were immovable.

The blade began to descend.

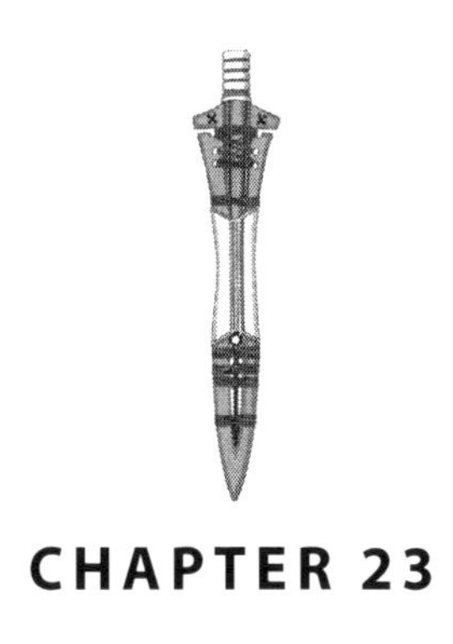

CHAPTER 23

In a blur of motion, Gabriel exploded into action.

He wrenched himself free of his captors with inhuman strength, bursting through their ranks, moving like a warrior possessed. He was a being of unbridled fury that knew no fear, no mercy.

No restraint.

The soldiers on either side of him crumpled to the ground in pools of blood, their mortal wounds sustained in between the beats of his heart.

Gabriel was somehow already on the dais — in front of the Spear, his body protecting Jake's — and as Stronghold plunged the blade down, it sank deep into Gabriel's chest instead.

Stronghold gasped. "No, it can't be…"

Gabriel bellowed his fury, a primal roar that shook the foundations of the chamber.

Those gathered fell silent before his rage.

He seemed to grow in stature as he loomed over Stronghold, his hands gripping the general's, still holding the Spear within his chest.

The shades of the dead SS swirled around Gabriel in a maelstrom of unholy energy, their ethereal forms twisting and writhing. They seeped into his skin, infusing him with a terrifying, dark power. His eyes blazed with an otherworldly light, his skin crackling with the occult energy that surged through his veins.

With a bend of his wrist, Gabriel wrenched Stronghold's hand away from the blade, leaving it embedded in his chest.

As they struggled, they spun around, and Morgan glimpsed the wound.

Blood welled around the blade and as the crimson drops touched the metal, a ripping sound rang through the chamber.

The veil of reality split.

A ragged portal tore open in a seething, swirling vortex of dark energy.

Demon hordes on a burning plain surged toward the open gate in a mob of twisted flesh and foul intent. They seemed drawn to Gabriel, to the dark power that flowed through his veins and the weapon that was now an extension of his being. The demonic seed flowered within him and he alone had the power to wield the Spear and command the legions of Hell.

The sound of unholy shrieks and howls filled the chamber. Chaos broke loose as those gathered turned to run, desperately trying to escape the oncoming swarm.

Gabriel forced Stronghold to his knees.

The general's face was a mask of terror, his eyes wide and bulging as he stared up at the towering figure.

In one swift, brutal motion, Gabriel ripped the Spear from his own chest, tearing the jagged blade free. His blood spattered the stone floor in a crimson arc, the droplets sizzling and hissing on the altar, and almost immediately, the wound began to heal.

Gabriel raised the Spear to the general's neck, the blade now wrapped in twisted curls of smoke as it touched his beating pulse.

"Please, Gabriel," Stronghold begged. "Spare me, and my

armies will fight at your command. You have my allegiance. Please."

The surrounding shadows spun into a frenzied storm of darkness and raging chaos. The demonic horde howled with an unquenchable hunger for blood, their shrieks and grunts rising to a deafening crescendo.

They were almost at the portal, almost at the threshold between this world and whatever hellish place they dwelled in.

Morgan imagined the demons invading the bodies of those gathered here, some of the most powerful people in the country, and then onward into the massed crowd above. Those already prepared for violence would turn dark desires into savage reality. If Gabriel embraced the demonic side of his heritage, the world that the Nazis intended to conjure would soon be a reality.

There was only one chance left.

Morgan sprinted toward the altar, trying to reach the man she knew in her heart was honorable.

"Choose life, Gabriel," she shouted above the din. "Choose. Life."

A soldier tackled her to the floor with a sickening thud.

Morgan lay winded beneath him, looking up to witness whatever might come.

Gabriel held the blade inches from the general's neck, ready to slice deep and wash the altar in a red veil of sacrificial blood. The Spear quivered in his grasp like a living thing, as if it yearned to light a spark of conflict that would tear a generation apart.

Gabriel let out a quick breath, blinked, shook his head.

With a shuddering gasp, he lowered the Spear, the blade still held in his hand but now without threat.

"I choose life." His words echoed through the chamber.

The demons beyond the veil shrieked in frustration and rage as the portal began to shudder and dissipate into smoke.

Gabriel staggered back, his chest heaving, his eyes clearing from the berserker madness that had possessed him moments before.

He reached down and dragged the soldier off Morgan before helping her up.

They stood in front of the crumpled figure of General Stronghold as the shadows whirled closer around him in a maelstrom of darkness. The sinister figures within, skull rings glinting, seemed to draw the very life force from him.

Stronghold sagged on his knees, clutching at his chest as if his heart was torn asunder. His face grew ashen, and the light faded from his eyes until they were dull and listless.

His followers and soldiers watched in horror as their once mighty leader was reduced to a husk of a man, a shattered remnant of his former glory. His bid for ultimate power lay in ruins, and the Spear was no longer his to command.

One by one, they turned away, their faces etched with disappointment and disillusionment. Silently, they filed out of the chamber, leaving Stronghold kneeling by the altar, broken and humiliated.

Gabriel and Morgan released Jake from his bonds; together, they hobbled from the chamber, back up the stairs and out into the square.

It was almost empty now. Banners bearing the general's likeness lay trampled in the mud, his face obscured by grime and filth. Those who had chanted so fervently now drifted away, their dreams of violent conquest shattered.

As Morgan stood with Jake and Gabriel facing the Capitol, the wind lifted the Stars and Stripes flag so it flew straight, a symbol of enduring freedom. The storm clouds parted and a shaft of sunlight shone down, illuminating the Capitol dome with bands of gold.

CHAPTER 24

Morgan and Gabriel hurried through the hallways of the John Radcliffe hospital in Oxford. They had flown straight from Washington, DC, leaving Jake behind to recover from his injuries under the expert care of ARKANE's medical team.

It was almost two a.m. and the hospital was quiet, the stillness broken only by the distant beep of monitors and the hushed whispers of the night shift. Gabriel carried a satchel slung over his shoulder, the Spear inside, wrapped in layers of protective cloth. Morgan was almost hyperaware of it, sensing its current like static electricity dancing across her skin, raising the fine hairs on her arms. She could only imagine how Gabriel felt with the relic so close to him, its power now awakened.

ARKANE Director Marietti had ordered Morgan to bring the Spear back so it could be studied and then locked away inside a high security vault to keep it safe. She had agreed in order to get them on a private jet, but she couldn't control Gabriel, and there was something far more important they needed to do with the Spear.

They reached the end of the corridor near Gemma's room, the soft glow of monitors visible through the half open door. They turned a corner out of sight, and Morgan pulled out her phone, dialing Faye's number.

Her sister answered quickly.

"Morgan, are you almost here? She's fading fast."

"I'm downstairs, but they won't let me up. Can you come to the front desk and vouch for me?"

There was a moment of hesitation on the other end of the line. "I don't want to leave her. What if—"

"It will only take a few minutes. Please, Faye. I need to see her."

A heartbeat passed, then another, before Faye spoke, her voice thick with unshed tears. "Alright. I'm coming now."

Morgan ended the call, her hand trembling as she slipped the phone back into her pocket. After a moment, Faye walked out of Gemma's room, pulling the door shut behind her as she hurried away down the hall. She would only be gone ten minutes, if that. They didn't have much time.

With Gabriel close behind, Morgan slipped into Gemma's hospital room. Her breath caught in her throat as she approached the bed, blinking away tears at the sight of her niece.

Gemma lay still and silent, her skin pale as bone against the starched white sheets. The monitors beeped a steady rhythm, the only sound in the room apart from the soft hiss of the ventilator that breathed for her. She looked so tiny, so fragile. Morgan's heart wrenched with the knowledge that it was her blood poisoning Gemma, her actions that caused such suffering.

But if this sickness truly resulted from an otherworldly curse, then Morgan had to believe that a supernatural relic could heal the damage.

"Let's do this." Gabriel stepped close to the bed, reached into the satchel, and withdrew the Spear.

Shafts of moonlight filtered through the hospital window, glinting off the blade in a shimmering dance of light and shadow as the metal seemed to pulse with life.

Morgan sensed the thrum of its power in her own still-cursed blood, an ancient energy that promised miracles and damnation in equal measure. Her breath caught in her throat as Gabriel gently placed the cool metal of the Spear flat against Gemma's bare arm. The ancient weapon, the cause of so much violence and war, now rested against the fragile skin of an innocent child.

Gabriel kept one hand on the Spear, his fingers curling around the hilt as he bowed his head.

Morgan hoped he was praying, not to the demonic forces they had faced in the depths of the Capitol, but to the God he still believed in, the one who had guided his path and led him to this moment. Perhaps he called on the angels, those who carried out the will of the Almighty, to lend their strength to this desperate act of faith.

While she did not believe in that God herself, Morgan whispered the Mi Shebeirach prayer for healing, the Hebrew words forming on her lips as a talisman against the shadow of death.

Outside the hospital, high above them, storm clouds gathered once more, dark forms swirling against the inky sky. Winged creatures flitted through the shadows, their ethereal forms barely visible in the gloom. Morgan shivered, feeling the weight of their presence, the unspoken threat that hung heavy in the air, in a battle for the blood of the living.

Gabriel gasped, his fingers gripping the Spear as a dark stain rose on Gemma's arm. The twisting mass writhed under her skin, pulsing with a hideous semblance of life. It seeped onto the blade of the Spear, like a line of thick tar drawn out of the little girl's body into the ancient metal, attracted by some resonant power.

The stain traveled up the blade, snaking its way to Gabriel's hand. He clenched his teeth, his face contorting in a grimace of pain as the darkness entered his veins, turning his arm a mottled shade of bruised black.

As the searing fire of the curse bonded with his tainted

blood, Morgan felt a sudden, sharp tug inside, a sensation of something being ripped away.

She doubled over in pain as it wrenched through her.

"Touch the metal," Gabriel gasped. "It's okay. I can contain it."

Morgan reached out and placed her fingertips on the Spear, breathless as the pull of its energy tugged at the dark curse inside. She felt something unwind from around her heart, the malevolent tendrils slowly losing their grip.

The pain intensified, as if the malign curse did not want to give up its unwilling host.

Gabriel clenched the Spear more tightly, each breath a ragged gasp — until suddenly, it was over.

What remained of the oozing pitch was absorbed into the ancient metal, which turned to dull grey once more.

The stain faded from Gabriel's limbs.

Almost immediately, color returned to Gemma's skin, her arms looking a more healthy pink, her cheeks beginning to bloom. The vital signs on the monitors ticked upward, the steady beep of the heart rate monitor growing stronger with every second.

Gabriel lifted the Spear away from Gemma's arm and slipped it back into his satchel.

The act of healing had clearly taken a toll on him. The lines of pain were more deeply etched into his face, and he sagged as if he bore a heavier weight now. But there was also a glimmer of wonder in his eyes as he looked down at the child he had helped rescue from the arms of death.

Gabriel had proved that the Spear could be used for healing as well as destruction, and Morgan knew she should take it from him, as Marietti had directed her. But in witnessing its potential power, she sensed humanity would be better off if the weapon remained with someone who understood what it could do. The ARKANE vault had been breached in the past, and many would seek the Spear again. It would be better off with Gabriel. Back in the crypt below the Capitol, he had chosen life, and she had to trust he would make the same choice again if he had to.

Footsteps echoed in the corridor and Faye burst in through the door, her features gaunt and etched with worry. Her eyes widened at Morgan standing beside Gemma's bed, and then narrowed as she saw Gabriel.

"Morgan, you're here. I was worried," she said, her voice a mixture of relief and confusion as she looked up at Gabriel. "And who are you?"

He straightened, his hand tightening on the strap of his satchel. "I'm a friend of Morgan's. My name's Gabriel."

Faye smiled, her features transforming with the light of the faith she held so dear. "Like the angel. Your name means God is my strength."

Gabriel nodded as he walked to the door. "I hope He can be your strength. Now, I'll leave you with your family."

Faye turned away from him, her arms outstretched as she embraced Morgan. As the sisters held each other, Gabriel walked out through the doorway into the harsh fluorescent light of the corridor beyond.

Morgan pulled away from her sister, a sudden urgency driving her after him.

She dashed out into the hallway. "Gabriel, wait!"

He turned, his gaze meeting hers. Morgan glimpsed the man beneath the warrior, forged in the fires of violence and now tempered by the weight of destiny.

"You could join us, you know?" The words tumbled out in a rush. "You could become an ARKANE agent. Help us defeat other human and supernatural forces. It doesn't have to be over."

Gabriel shook his head. "I need to divide the Spear once more and sink the pieces far apart in the deep ocean. No one should ever command this much power again. Not even me." He gave a wry smile. "It might go a different way next time."

He paused, his gaze growing distant, as if he could see beyond the confines of the hospital walls. "Then I want to find others like me, those born from demonic seeds. I'll use the records you gave me from Wewelsburg to find them."

Morgan nodded. "And then?"

He shrugged, a gesture that spoke of a future still unwritten. "Maybe I'll come and find you."

Morgan closed the distance between them, her arms reaching out to pull him into a tight embrace. They stood for a moment, holding each other, breathing together. This chapter was over for her, but it was just the beginning of his journey.

"Thank you, Gabriel," she whispered. "And remember, choose life."

From the hospital room behind them, Faye's excited voice rang out. "Morgan, come quickly! She's waking up!"

Morgan pulled away from Gabriel, her heart racing as she turned toward the hospital room. At the door, she looked back one last time.

Gabriel smiled, a genuine smile this time, one that lit up his face and made him look younger, more at peace. "Go," he said, his voice soft but insistent.

Morgan turned and dashed back into the hospital room, her breath catching in her throat as Gemma stirred on the bed, fighting the tube that snaked down her throat. Faye was at her daughter's side, clutching Gemma's hand, her eyes bright with tears.

A doctor rushed in, his hands moving with practiced efficiency as he removed the tube from Gemma's throat. The little girl coughed and sputtered, her chest heaving as she drew in gulps of air.

Faye gathered Gemma into her arms, rocking her back and forth as she murmured words of comfort and love. Gemma's eyes fluttered open, her gaze finding Morgan's across the room. She smiled weakly and reached out toward her aunt.

As Morgan took Gemma's hand and wrapped her arms around her sister and her niece, a wave of relief washed over her, and light bloomed inside.

She knew, with a certainty that defied explanation, that the curse of the Black Anchorite had been broken. She could feel it in her body, in the flow of her blood, and in the steady beat of her heart. The shadow that haunted her was gone, banished by the power of the Spear and the honor of the one who wielded it.

As the doctor ran more tests, checking Gemma's vital signs and assessing her condition, Morgan walked to the window. The first light of dawn was breaking over the spires of Oxford, painting the sky in shades of coral pink and gold.

She glimpsed Gabriel walking through the square below, striding into the new day. Perhaps their paths would cross again. In a world where ancient relics held the power to heal and destroy, where the lines between good and evil were often blurred, anything was possible.

THE END

AUTHOR'S NOTE

It's been several years since my last ARKANE novel, *Tomb of Relics*, although I wrote a short story, *Soldiers of God*, in the interim.

My readers often urge me to write faster, but my ARKANE thrillers have a particular restriction. They are all based on actual places and real historic events that I twist into a thriller with elements of the supernatural. These stories take time to emerge because I have to find the threads of the story in the real world first.

Here's how *Spear of Destiny* originated, and you can find this online with clickable links at www.jfpenn.com/destinyresearch

Finding an initial story thread in Vienna

Most of my books are based on places I've visited, or researched in depth, and I've been wanting to go to Vienna for a long time. At the end of *Tomb of Relics*, Jake is heading there for another mission, and Morgan has been cursed by the Black Anchorite, so I knew those two elements had to start the next book.

I also wanted to weave in Washington, DC somehow, since I visited the city in early 2023, so the initial challenge was finding a religious relic or a story thread that linked the two places.

I started reading about Vienna and the history of the Habsburg dynasty, as well as the early days of psychiatry. But I've already featured Sigmund Freud's influence in *Ark of Blood*, so I focused on the religious elements of the city instead.

As I researched the various museums in Vienna, I discovered that the Spear of Destiny — or at least one of the relics that are purported to be the spear — was in the Hofburg museum complex.

I read books about the Spear and learned it had fascinated Adolf Hitler when he lived in Vienna as a young man, and then I found out that Heinrich Himmler, head of the SS elite soldiers, had been obsessed with the occult. The Spear of Destiny clearly has a fascinating history — so it became my MacGuffin, the object that centers the plot in action adventure thrillers.

Visiting Vienna and Nuremberg, February 2024

On the first morning of my multi-day trip, I went to the Schatzkammer, the treasury of the Hofburg museum: www.kaiserliche-schatzkammer.at

The description in Chapter 2 is based on my visit, and the place really was completely empty. I stood alone before the Spear (which is in the same room as the tooth of John the Baptist!) and couldn't believe there wasn't more information about its fascinating history. For obvious reasons, Austria and Germany prefer not to focus on the dark history of the Nazi regime, but there was nothing about the religious mythology behind the lance or the other kings who had claimed its power.

I walked out of the treasury and through a corridor, emerging next to the National Library and State Hall, which I entered on a whim since I was passing.

www.onb.ac.at/en/museums/state-hall

I'm so glad I went in as the library is truly stunning. As I walked through, I imagined a fight scene there, which turned into Chapter 3.

The Monument Against War and Fascism in the opening of Chapter 5 is also real, and just as disturbing as described.

There are some other fascinating places in Vienna. I particularly enjoyed visiting St Stephen's Cathedral and the Kapuzinergruft, the Capuchin crypt with the tombs of the Habsburg royalty, but they didn't make it into the book.

I've been as accurate as possible with the dates of historical events. In 1933, Hitler became Chancellor of Germany and then Führer, and in 1938 declared the Anschluss, the annexation of the Federal State of Austria into the German Reich.

On 13 October 1938, the Holy Lance and the other Habsburg imperial regalia were taken to Nuremberg under SS guard and housed in St Catherine's Church. Heinrich Himmler was Reichsführer of the SS at the time, so this would have been under his direction.

The Allies took control of Nuremberg and the Spear on 20 April 1945, and Hitler committed suicide in his bunker in Berlin ten days later on 30 April 1945.

It's only a few hours on the fast train from Vienna to Nuremberg, so well worth a visit if you're in that area. Train travel is easy in Europe and one of the best ways to get around. I used the Trainline app to book tickets, which I also use in the UK.

I didn't have long in Nuremberg, so I went straight to the art bunker for a tour, which takes about ninety minutes. Chapter 6 is based on that visit and everything is as Jake describes, including the photo of Hitler in front of the Spear and the plans for the Congress Hall. It's an excellent tour and you need to book in advance at museums.nuernberg.de/world-war-art-bunker/visitor-services/guided-tours.

In the same area, you can visit the Dürer house, where

Albrecht Dürer made his wood blocks and Apocalypse prints, among other artworks, which feature in *Crypt of Bone*. More details at:

museums.nuernberg.de/albrecht-duerer-house

Just down the hill, I recommend St Sebald's church, where a ring of snails support the saint's shrine. You can find some pictures on my Instagram:

www.instagram.com/p/C2nhtg5ryaA/

There are more photos and practical details in my overview article, "Vienna, Nuremberg, and Cologne. My Five Day Research Trip for Spear of Destiny":

www.booksandtravel.page/vienna-nuremberg-cologne/

Hitler, Himmler, Wewelsburg, and Nazi occult interest in the Spear of Destiny

I read books around this area as listed in the Bibliography below, and one of the most fascinating was *Adolf Hitler and the Secrets of the Holy Lance*, written by two soldiers who fought in World War II on opposite sides. From a second-hand store in Germany, I managed to source a first edition signed by one of the authors, Colonel Howard A. Buechner, Battalion Surgeon. It's co-written with Captain Wilhelm Bernhart, Reich Undersea Boat Service, Knight of the Holy Lance.

The book includes sketches of the Spear and the runes that (supposedly) control its power, as well as legends of the Lance prior to World War II, extensive details about Himmler, Wewelsburg, and more.

Adolf Hitler, an Austrian, was rejected from the Academy of Fine Arts in Vienna but remained in the city painting and selling his work in the early 1900s. While he was there, he studied the Lance and learned about the occult. He reportedly underlined a quote in a book, *Magic: History, Theory and Practice* by Ernst Schertel, which reads: "He who does not carry demonic seeds within him will never give birth to a new world."

I added this quote to the altar under Wewelsburg Castle and used it as the basis for Gabriel's supernatural abilities, but of course, the basement crypt is my invention and there is no evidence of demons summoned there.

Other stories based on similar inspiration include the *Hellboy* universe, the game *Castle Wolfenstein*, and *Indiana Jones*.

You can find out more about Wewelsburg Castle and Himmler's plans for it at www.wewelsburg.de

Unfortunately, I didn't find out about the castle until after I returned from Vienna, so I didn't visit in person, but I researched thoroughly with books and online sources.

The Hall of the Supreme Leaders and the Black Sun mosaic is real with the quote as described over its entrance, 'my house will be called a house of prayer,' from Isaiah chapter 56:7. The complete verse reads, "Their burnt offerings and sacrifices will be accepted on my altar; for my house will be called a house of prayer for all nations."

The 'burnt offerings and sacrifices' clearly echo the millions killed in Nazi concentration camps, so perhaps this was a deliberate use of the quote, yet I couldn't find mention of this in anyone else's research.

Lhasa, Tibet

The Ahnenerbe scientists, under Himmler's direction, went on many research trips and in 1938, the German explorer Ernst Schafer led a group to Tibet. The regent welcomed them into the sacred city of Lhasa and they spent several months studying in the library and taking anatomical measurements of Tibetan people.

The anthropologist Bruno Beger did indeed collect skulls later on and was convicted of eighty-six counts of accessory to murder during the Nuremberg trials of 1946.

Although I haven't visited Lhasa, I spent a lot of time researching the Potala Palace and the journey to the city via the Qinghai–Tibet Railway, a beautiful, slow route that helps travelers adjust to the altitude.

There is extensive restoration and translation work in the ancient library under Chinese direction. You can watch a video about it here: www.jfpenn.com/potalalibrary

The Vesuvius Prize that Tenzin mentions is real, and it's incredible to think that AI technology is now helping decipher these carbonised scrolls. You can read more at Scrollprize.org

I find the scanning of ancient texts endlessly fascinating, and a similar Vatican project inspired my short story *Soldiers of God*, if you like this kind of thing, too!

I mainly used *Himmler's Crusade* by Christopher Hale as research for this section, and also a documentary, *Secret Nazi Expeditions: Tibet.*

One of the most rewarding things as an author comes from the moment of synchronicity, when everything lines up, and the story could actually be possible based on research. It's the moment I look forward to in every book, and it always comes.

My moment of synchronicity for this book arrived during the Tibet research as I discovered that the 'rushes,' the original pre-edited footage, lay within the Schäfer Collection in the Library of Congress in Washington, DC, which also has the Third Reich Collection, and Hitler's personal library.

Washington, DC, USA

I visited the city in January 2023 and had a wonderful few days touring museums and also the Library of Congress.

Although I didn't go inside the Capitol, I walked through the large park at the back where the rally happens in Chapter 4. The crypt underneath the Capitol is my invention, as are the characters and Jericho Command.

I explored the Library of Congress, which is full of beautiful mosaics, murals, and literary quotes as well as special reading rooms. I didn't have this book in mind at the time so I didn't apply for access to the Nazi Archives or anything related to Operation Paperclip, the US intelligence program that allowed over 1,600 Nazi scientists to escape justice in order to continue their research.

Kurt Blome was the director of the Nazi biological warfare program and carried out experiments on inmates in concentration camps. Despite the evidence against him, he was acquitted of war crimes at Nuremberg based on intervention from the US military.

Fort Detrick is a real US Army command base. It was the centre of the US biological weapons program after World War II, and is now home to various departments, including the US Army Medical Research Institute of Infectious Diseases (USAMRIID) and more.

You can find more pictures of my trip in my article "Classical Architecture, Angels Unawares, And A Surprise Gutenberg Bible. A Long Weekend In Washington DC USA": www.booksandtravel.page/washington-dc-usa/

Bibliography and Further Research:

Adolf Hitler and the Secrets of the Holy Lance —
Col. Howard A. Buechner and Capt. Wilhelm Bernhart

Blitzed: Drugs in Nazi Germany — Norman Ohler

"Heinrich Himmler." Holocaust Encyclopedia, accessed 24 Feb 2024 — https://encyclopedia.ushmm.org/content/en/article/heinrich-himmler

Himmler's Crusade: The Nazi Expedition to Find the Origins of the Aryan Race — Christopher Hale

"Hitler's Forgotten Library" — Timothy W. Ryback, *The Atlantic*, May 2003, www.theatlantic.com/magazine/archive/2003/05/hitlers-forgotten-library/302727/

Hitler's Holy Relics: A True Story of Nazi Plunder and the Race to Recover the Crown Jewels of the Holy Roman Empire — Sidney Kirkpatrick

Hitler's Monsters: Supernatural History of the Third Reich — Eric Kurlander

Operation Paperclip: The Secret Intelligence Program that Brought Nazi Scientists to America — Annie Jacobsen

Schäfer collection and Third Reich collection, Library of Congress, Washington, DC, www.loc.gov/item/2010651980/ and www.loc.gov/item/2009632506/

Secret Nazi Expeditions: Tibet. History Play documentary on Amazon Prime

The Devil's Disciples: The Lives and Times of Hitler's Inner Circle — Anthony Read

The Nazi Occult — Kenneth Hite

The Spear of Destiny — Trevor Ravenscroft

The True Cross and the Spear of Destiny — Gustavo Vazquez Lozano & Charles River

Vienna: The International Capital — Angus Robertson

ENJOYED SPEAR OF DESTINY?

Thanks for joining Morgan and Jake
on another ARKANE adventure.

If you loved the book and have a moment to spare,
I would really appreciate a short review on the
page where you bought the book.

Your help in spreading the word is gratefully
appreciated and reviews make a huge difference to
helping new readers find the series. Thank you!

Get a free ebook copy of the bestselling thriller, *Day of the Vikings*, ARKANE book 5, when you sign up to join my Reader's Group. You'll also be notified of new releases, giveaways and receive personal updates from behind the scenes of my thrillers and photos from my research trips.

Just go to: www.JFPenn.com/free

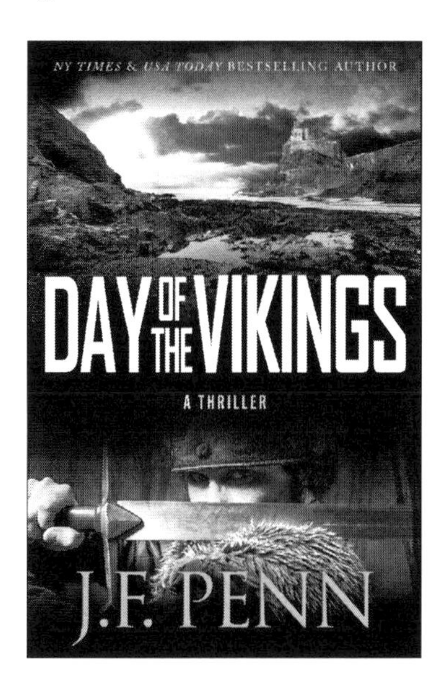

Day of the Vikings, an ARKANE thriller

A ritual murder on a remote island under the shifting skies of the aurora borealis.

A staff of power that can summon Ragnarok, the Viking apocalypse.

When Neo-Viking terrorists invade the British Museum in London to reclaim the staff of Skara Brae, ARKANE agent Dr. Morgan Sierra is trapped in the building along with hostages under mortal threat.

As the slaughter begins, Morgan works alongside psychic Blake Daniel to discern the past of the staff, dating back to islands invaded by the Vikings generations ago.

Can Morgan and Blake uncover the truth before Ragnarok is unleashed, consuming all in its wake?

Day of the Vikings is a fast-paced, supernatural thriller set in London and the islands of Orkney, Lindisfarne and Iona. Set in the present day, it resonates with the history and myth of the Vikings.

If you love an action-packed thriller, you can get *Day of the Vikings* (ebook) for free now:

WWW.JFPENN.COM/FREE

Day of the Vikings features Dr. Morgan Sierra from the ARKANE thrillers, and Blake Daniel from the Brooke and Daniel Psychological/Crime Thrillers, but it is also a standalone novella that can be read and enjoyed separately.

ACKNOWLEDGMENTS

Thanks to my readers. I hope this satisfies the need for another ARKANE adventure with Morgan and Jake, at least until next time!

Thanks to my editor Kristen Tate at The Blue Garret, and my book designer, Jane at JD Smith Design.

Thanks to my brother Thom Penn for making my research trip to Nuremberg more fun, and for Holger Nils Pohl for joining me in the dark conversations that inevitably arose based on the topic of the book.

MORE BOOKS AND AUDIOBOOKS BY J.F.PENN

ARKANE Action-Adventure Thrillers

Stone of Fire #1
Crypt of Bone #2
Ark of Blood #3
One Day in Budapest #4
Day of the Vikings #5
Gates of Hell #6
One Day in New York #7
Destroyer of Worlds #8
End of Days #9
Valley of Dry Bones #10
Tree of Life #11
Tomb of Relics #12
[Stand-alone ARKANE story — Soldiers of God]
Spear of Destiny #13

Brooke and Daniel Psychological/Crime Thrillers

Desecration #1
Delirium #2
Deviance #3

Mapwalker Dark Fantasy Adventures

Map of Shadows #1
Map of Plagues #2
Map of the Impossible #3

Short Stories

A Thousand Fiendish Angels
The Dark Queen
A Midwinter Sacrifice
Blood, Sweat, and Flame
With a Demon's Eye
Beneath the Zoo

Travel Memoir

Pilgrimage: Lessons Learned from
Solo Walking Three Ancient Ways

Other Books

Catacomb

Risen Gods — co-written with J. Thorn

American Demon Hunters: Sacrifice — co-written with J. Thorn, Lindsay Buroker, and Zach Bohannon

More books coming soon …

You can sign up to be notified of new releases, giveaways and pre-release specials - plus, get a free ebook!

WWW.JFPENN.COM/FREE

If you loved the book and have a moment to spare, I would really appreciate a short review on the page where you bought the book.

Your help in spreading the word is gratefully appreciated and reviews make a huge difference to helping new readers find the series.

Thank you!

ABOUT J.F. PENN

J.F. Penn is the Award-winning, New York Times and USA Today bestselling author of the ARKANE action adventure thrillers, Brooke & Daniel psychological/crime thrillers, the Map- walker fantasy adventure series, travel memoir, as well as other standalone stories.

Her books weave together ancient artifacts, relics of power, international locations, and adventure with an edge of the supernatural.

Jo lives in Bath, England and enjoys a nice G&T.

You can find my J.F. Penn Reading Order at:
www.jfpenn.com/readingorder

Buy books directly from me:

www.JFPennBooks.com

* * *

Sign up for your free thriller, *Day of the Vikings*, and receive updates from behind the scenes, research, and giveaways at:

WWW.JFPENN.COM/FREE

* * *

Connect with Joanna:
www.JFPenn.com
joanna@JFPenn.com
www.Facebook.com/JFPennAuthor
www.Instagram.com/JFPennAuthor
www.BooksAndTravel.page

* * *

For writers:

Joanna's site, www.TheCreativePenn.com empowers authors with the knowledge they need to choose their creative future. Books and courses by Joanna Penn, as well as her award-winning show, *The Creative Penn Podcast*, provide information and inspiration on how to write, publish and market books, and make a living as a writer.